DARWIN

Ch. Darwin

DARWIN

BY

GAMALIEL BRADFORD

WITH ILLUSTRATIONS

BOSTON AND NEW YORK

HOUGHTON MIFFLIN COMPANY

The Riverside Press Cambridge

1926

The Riverside Press
CAMBRIDGE · MASSACHUSETTS
PRINTED IN THE U.S.A.

TO

MARSHALL LIVINGSTON PERRIN
WHO TAUGHT ME TO WRITE
AND TO THINK

On se lasse de tout sauf de comprendre

SAINTE-BEUVE (from Virgil?)

CONTENTS

I. THE OBSERVER   3

II. THE THINKER   44

III. THE DISCOVERER   83

IV. THE LOSER   128

V. THE LOVER   168

VI. THE DESTROYER   208

VII. THE SCIENTIFIC SPIRIT   248

INDEX   307

ILLUSTRATIONS

CHARLES DARWIN   *Frontispiece*

    Photograph taken in 1881 by Elliott & Fry, London, reproduced in
    More Letters of Charles Darwin

CHARLES DARWIN AS A CHILD WITH HIS SISTER
    CATHERINE   4

    From a chalk drawing reproduced in *Emma Darwin: A Century of
    Family Letters*

THE BEAGLE LAID ASHORE FOR REPAIRS AT RIVER
    SANTA CRUZ, PATAGONIA   14

    From *Life and Letters of Charles Darwin*

DOWN HOUSE FROM THE GARDEN   44

    From a woodcut in *The Century Magazine* reproduced in *Life and
    Letters*

FACSIMILE OF A PAGE FROM A NOTEBOOK OF 1837   88

    From *Life and Letters*

THE STUDY AT DOWN   128

    From a woodcut in *The Century Magazine* reproduced in *Life and
    Letters*

EMMA DARWIN AT THIRTY-ONE   190

    From the portrait painted by George Richmond, R.A., reproduced
    in *Emma Darwin*

CHARLES DARWIN ABOUT 1854   248

    Photograph by Maull & Fox, reproduced in *More Letters*

DARWIN

CHRONOLOGY

CHARLES ROBERT DARWIN

Born, Shrewsbury, February 12, 1809.

At Edinburgh University, 1826.

At Cambridge, 1827–1831.

Absent with the Beagle, 1831–1836.

Married Emma Wedgwood, January 29, 1839.

Settled at Down, in Kent, 1842.

'The Origin of Species' published, November 24, 1859.

'The Descent of Man' published, February 24, 1871.

Died, Down, April 19, 1882.

DARWIN

CHAPTER I

THE OBSERVER

I

ANY formal life of Darwin should be written by a thoroughly trained and equipped scientist, and indeed no such life could be better than that written by Darwin's son forty years ago. But one who, without special scientific qualifications, is profoundly interested in the characters and souls of men, all men, may perhaps be justified in making an intimate study of a man whose influence upon other men, for good and evil both, has been enormous, and who was himself one of the simplest, purest, noblest, most candid, most lovable, most Christian souls that ever lived.

By an extraordinary coincidence Charles Robert Darwin was born in Shrewsbury, England, on the same day, February 12, 1809, on which Abraham Lincoln was born in Hardin County, Kentucky. Darwin belonged to an excellent old English family on his father's side and his mother was one of the

Wedgwoods, of ceramic fame. His paternal grandfather, Erasmus, was a physician, a poet, and a
scientist. Darwin's father was an able and successful physician. He would have liked his son to be the
same, but the son had not the taste for it. Failing
medicine, the church was considered, but seemed
equally unpromising. Education at Edinburgh and
at Cambridge did not yield very much. In those
days the classics were the basis and this boy had
little interest in the classics. He liked field sports
and outdoor life. Above all, he liked animals and
plants, liked to observe and to describe them, and
to record his observations, and this interest grew
more and more absorbing.

In 1831, at the age of twenty-two, Darwin obtained the position of naturalist on the government
ship, Beagle, and for five years he was absent from
England, exploring the southern hemisphere and
carefully recording his observations on every sort of
scientific subject, which were later published in his
printed journal. Soon after his return home, he
married his cousin, Emma Wedgwood, a noble and
charming woman, and a little later, in 1842, he
settled at the small village of Down, in the county
of Kent, and made his home there until his death in
1882. He inherited a considerable property, which

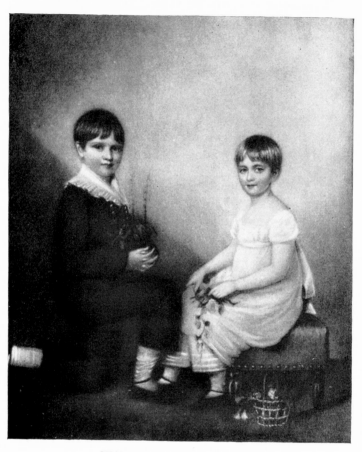

CHARLES DARWIN AS A CHILD
With his sister Catherine

was later increased from his books. He had a large family of sons and daughters, ten in all, and his life was half chronic invalidism and half intense devotion to scientific study and thought, or rather, the two elements were inextricably intertwined.

As a result of his observations on the Beagle, Darwin became possessed with the idea, which of course had occurred to various thinkers before him, from the Greeks to Lamarck, that life had not been created in distinct manifold forms, but had developed in all its variety, including even man, from a few forms, or even from one. To entertain the idea in the abstract was comparatively simple; but to explain the process of development was the puzzle, until Darwin hit upon what seemed to him the clue in what he called 'natural selection,' or, as Spencer termed it, 'the survival of the fittest.' For twenty years Darwin patiently worked out experimental proof of this theory, and then in 1859 he published 'The Origin of Species,' a book which is generally admitted to be one of the most important in the whole history of science. During the remaining twenty years of his life he devoted himself to endless further experiment, and the results were embodied in numerous volumes, chief among which was 'The Descent of Man.' His views were from the first the subject of fierce controversy, and in many details they are still so, and will continue to be. But it may safely be said that in the scientific world the evolution of life, or more technically, modification by descent, which is so inseparably associated with Darwin's name, is an accepted principle, and Darwin himself had the great and satisfying triumph of living until this acceptance was perceived to be general, if not universal. He was buried in Westminster Abbey, close to the last resting-place of Newton.

The basis, or at any rate one of the most fundamental elements of Darwin's character, was the instinct and habit of observing the external world, and we can best approach him by considering this habit in others and in him. It is astonishing how little most of us see. We live in a world of shadows and dream outlines, piecing out reality by convenient abstractions, which pass in memory like worn current counters, with little resemblance to actual fact. A tree to us is vaguely a tree: the structure of its bark, the shape of its leaves do not enter our world. A man and a woman are simply — a man and a woman. Unless we are specially called upon to do so we do not note details of feature or gesture or garment. This vagueness, this abstraction of vision, is what Théophile Gautier referred to in his celebrated phrase, 'I am a man for whom the visible world exists.'[1] And he amplified his idea by saying that of twenty-five persons who come into a room, twenty-four will go out and not be able to tell you the color of the wall-paper, whereas he could tell that and pretty much everything else. To such an observing temperament life is a matter of visual detail, of sensuous detail of every kind.

There are people who look out and people who look in, and of course there are all sorts of degrees between the two extremes. Some people are wholly preoccupied with their own inner life, their thoughts, their emotions, their experiences. It is only by the pressure of necessity that they force themselves into connection with the world about them, and then it is under protest, and their thoughts leap back, as by a spring, to internal matters, as soon as the pressure is removed. Others live in the swift, diverting movement of the external world and lose their own destiny and almost their identity in the play of it. 'Let me alone to observe till I turn myself into nothing but observation,' says the old poet.[2] The observation may be for a serious scientific purpose. It may be for endless entertainment and pure, inexhaustible delight. As Sterne

7

has it: 'What a large volume of adventures may be grasped within this little span of life by him who interests his heart in everything and who, having eyes to see what time and chance are perpetually holding out to him as he journeyeth on his way, misses nothing he can *fairly* lay his hands on.'[3]

As there are some persons who naturally observe, so there are some who observe certain things, and not others. Women are apt to be more acute observers than men: their senses are more keen and their minds less preoccupied. But their vision is usually limited to the things that interest them. A woman will go into a friend's house and tell you every detail of furnishing, will describe the friend's dress with finished minuteness. But she may take a walk through the fields and not be able to remember a single flower or insect. On the other hand, very great scientists will not miss a spider in the grass, but the color of a ribbon may escape them.

From another point of view observation may be deliberately exclusive. A trained observer may find that general vision distracts him, and that to follow up his special object it is necessary to put all other sights and sounds out of consideration entirely. Bradford Torrey used to say, and no doubt it is the experience of all naturalists, that if he went to look for a special flower, he saw flowers only, and was quite oblivious to birds, while on bird days a rare blossom might be passed unnoticed.

Naturally the most common matter of observation, the one which is more or less forced upon the attention of all of us, is humanity. We may be indifferent to trees and stones, but our pleasure, our labor, our existence depend upon a more or less constant study of the human beings whose existence interlocks at every point with ours. Therefore, from the earliest times of record there have been profound observers of humanity, persons who have examined the human aspect and the human heart, as read through that aspect, with the most persistent zeal and the most unwearying delight. In the vivid phrase of one of the most acute of these, 'I glutted myself with observation.' And even those of less gormandizing tendency find the analysis of the human subject one of the most inexhaustible pleasures that this world affords. All through the study of Darwin I shall have occasion to refer to one of Darwin's contemporaries who in a different line of research was an equally brilliant and significant exemplification of the scientific spirit, Sainte-Beuve. As Darwin devoted years upon years to patient investigation of the secrets of the natural world, so Sainte-Beuve with the same patience, the same labor, the same infinite and ever-varied curiosity, probed human hearts, all sorts of human hearts, and portrayed them with unfailing accuracy and sympathy. He said of himself, using the strictly scientific expression: 'I analyze, I herborize, I am a naturalist of souls.'[4]

But in dealing with Darwin we are in the main concerned with the field of so-called natural science, with the varying aspects of the material world, which we are apt to sum up under the term, nature. General observation of this world is, of course, also as old as man. Greek, Hebrew, Egyptian, all ancient records, contain scientific facts of importance and interest to-day. Sophocles and Vergil had an exquisite sense of the exact beauty of birds and flowers. The vision of Chaucer and Shakespeare was as acute as that of Gautier, so far as they chose to employ it. At the same time we must recognize that with the middle of the eighteenth century a new interest in nature arose. The literature of Rousseau and Cowper, of Keats and George Sand, reflected the external world in a far different fashion from anything before imagined, and Linnæus, Cuvier, and many others laid the foundations of modern scientific study, which the nineteenth century developed until it overshadowed every branch of learning both for theoretical abundance and for practical utility.

It must of course be recognized that in many cases the observation of nature is not practiced for the pure pleasure of it, but serves some ulterior object or interest. There is first the obvious practical gain from such observation. Agriculture has undergone a complete revolution in the last hundred years, and this revolution has been brought about by the various developments of scientific research. Darwin's vast investigations showed the intimate connection between the theories of the scientist and the practical experiments of the breeder.

On the other side there is the observation of the artist. Ruskin pointed out long ago, how fine, how subtle, how delicate was the vision of the great painters, how perfect their skill in rendering the exact sense impression of natural objects. In the same way, it is not often considered what wealth of accurate record we have in the poets and novelists. Gautier, for whom the visible world existed, was a poet. He saw shapes and contours and colors, saw them to render them in words that

II

Of the numerous records of simple natural observation and experience few are more charming than Darwin's 'Journal of the Voyage of the Beagle,' in which he notes what he saw and heard by land and sea during those years of adventure in the southern hemisphere. All through this book, as indeed in all his books, it is evident that the instinct and habit of observing were inborn and constant, and all those who write about Darwin make this instinct at least the foundation of his scientific eminence.

Asa Gray, who had given his life to botany, writes: 'What a skill and genius you have for these researches! Even for the structure of the flower of the Ophyrideæ I have to-night learned more than I ever knew before.'[7] Professor Osborn says, more generally: 'Rare as were his reasoning powers, his powers of observation were of a still more distinct order. He persistently and doggedly followed every clue; he noticed little things which escaped others; he always noted exceptions and at once jotted down facts opposed to his theories.'[8] And the editors of Darwin's letters put the whole matter with concise effectiveness in speaking of 'that supreme power of seeing and thinking what the rest of the world

THE BEAGLE LAID ASHORE FOR REPAIRS AT RIVER SANTA
CRUZ, PATAGONIA

had overlooked, which was one of his most striking characteristics.'[9]

Darwin's own comments on observation are frequent and most interesting. Little inclined as he was to self-praise, in the charming autobiographical sketch which begins the 'Life,' he frankly states his merits in this regard: 'I think that I am superior to the common run of men in noticing things which easily escape attention, and in observing them carefully. My industry has been nearly as great as it could have been in the observation and collection of facts.'[10] Exact, systematic, patient study of what is actually seen seems to him the basis of all great scientific work, and he repeatedly emphasizes the importance of it. 'It is well to remember that Naturalists value observations far more than reasoning.'[11] Again, 'I have come not to care at all for general beliefs without the special facts. I have suffered too often from this.'[12] And observation is not only a duty, it is a delight. The arrangement of facts, the deduction of theories from them, thought, reasoning, argument, these are labor and pain. But to watch the insects and the flowers, by long and careful attention to make them yield all their secrets, this is no labor, but an exquisite diversion, which never fails: 'A naturalist's life would be a happy one if he had only to observe, and never to write.'[13]

It is evident, further, that Darwin's observation was by no means confined to natural science, but was quick, acute, and constant in all the different phases and interests of life. Naturally his books deal with little besides his scientific work, but the record of the Beagle shows interest and appreciation of many things outside of this work altogether. An eye so carefully trained could not fail to distinguish and perceive all sorts of minute points that others would pass over. His readiness to note other things besides those he was looking for shows in the piquant comment on wide experimenting: 'It may turn out a mare's nest, but I have often incidentally observed curious facts when making what I call "a fool's experiment."'[14]

It is especially curious to note Darwin's observation of himself. To be sure, he disclaims any philosophical study in this regard: 'I have never tried looking into my own mind.'[15] Nevertheless, whether he tried or not, he was curiously alive to what went on there, and he records what he finds with the singular candor which appears in his treatment of his own affairs as well as of others. The very hesitation with which he speaks of self-analysis increases the value of his results: 'If I can analyze my own feelings (a very doubtful process).'[16] And when he does make a statement, it is all the more reliable and all the more far-reaching from the moderation and reserve with which it is advanced.

In one field quite remote from what is usually considered natural science, that of physiognomy and expression, Darwin's observation is especially interesting, though of course he connected this line of research, as so many others, with his general scientific theory. His book on 'The Expression of the Emotions' is one of the most entertaining and profitable of all for the general reader, and it is instructive to note, how early, how persistently, and how faithfully he collected memoranda on this comparatively collateral issue. The use of what was immediately about him, of his own personal experience in daily living, is especially significant in this regard. For the study of expression he felt that unconsciousness in the subject was a prime requisite. Hence the study of infants, who were perfectly indifferent to your investigations, was peculiarly profitable, and almost from the moment his children were born, Darwin began to make notes on their expressions of pain and pleasure, all the little subtle indications of desire and need, which mothers use instinctively but which fathers are not commonly apt to register as scientific data. The curious paper, published in *Mind*, called 'The Biography of a Child,' gives many of Darwin's notes on this subject, and repeated references in 'The Expression of the Emotions' show what fruitful use he made of those notes at a later period. The minuteness with which he observed and reflected is well shown in this passage on childrens' crying: 'I ought to have thought of crying children rubbing their eyes with their knuckles, but I did not think of it, and cannot explain it. As far as my memory serves, they do not do so whilst roaring, in which case compression would be of no use. . . . I wish I knew more about the knuckles and crying.'[17]

The observation not only records the larger and more violent manifestations of passion, but is constantly on the watch for those trifling signs of feeling which appear and flit away in trivial social intercourse. Take this account of an animated conversation: 'Another young lady and a youth, both in the highest spirits, were eagerly talking together with extraordinary rapidity; and I noticed that, as often as the young lady was beaten, and could not get out her words fast enough, her eyebrows went obliquely upwards, and rectangular furrows were formed on her forehead. She thus each time hoisted a flag of distress; and this she did half-a-dozen times in the course of a few minutes.'[18]

Nor is he content with his own observations, but in this, as in wider researches, he perpetually appeals to his friends for assistance, opens their eyes and sharpens their wits, to see and record matters which they would assuredly never have thought of for themselves. Note the care and tact with which he makes his requests: 'I beg you, *in relation to a new point for observation*, to imagine as well as you can that you suddenly come across some dreadful object, and act with a sudden little start, *a shudder of horror;* please do this once or twice, and observe yourself as well as you can, and *afterwards* read the rest of this note, which I have consequently pinned down.'[19]

It is, however, in the regions of natural science more particularly so-called that Darwin's observation is inexhaustibly rich, varied, exciting, and suggestive. He himself puts it very simply and effectively, when he says, 'I was born a naturalist.'[20] At the age of ten his curiosity was intensely stimulated by the varying aspects of insects and he con-

sidered the desirability of collecting them. In one
of his letters, Darwin gives an amusing illustration
of this youthful enthusiasm for collecting. One day
he had caught two most interesting beetles and
was holding one in each hand, when he discovered
a third, 'a sacred *Panagæus crux-major!*' 'I could
not bear to give up either of my *Carabi*, and to lose
Panagæus was out of the question; so that in despair I gently seized one of the *Carabi* between my
teeth, when to my unspeakable disgust and pain the
little inconsiderate beast squirted his acid down my
throat, and I lost both *Carabi* and *Panagæus.*'[21]

The delight of observation, which began in
childhood, continued to old age, and increased instead of weakening. When he was fatigued and
worn with writing and theorizing, when illness tormented him and weakness rendered more concentrated effort impossible, it was a relief to turn to the
simple contemplation of facts, and the budding and
fading of flowers and the varied activity of insects
offered at all times diversion and contentment.
Sometimes he dwells upon the larger aspects of such
contemplation, the joy of discovery, the excitement
of finding what has never been found before.
Again and again in his southern voyages this excitement appears: 'In these wild countries it gives

much delight to gain the summit of any mountain. There is an indefinite expectation of seeing something very strange, which, however often it may be balked, never failed with me to recur on each successive attempt.'[22] Or the pleasure may come in what seem the humblest, smallest things, in what is to ordinary persons negligible, or even repulsive. One of Darwin's most attractive books, perhaps with 'The Expression of the Emotions,' the most attractive from the casual reader's standpoint, is that in which he gathers together the results of his study of earthworms, a study which had continued through years of patient and thoughtful investigation of a subject which, even from the naturalist's point of view, would not seem one of the most fruitful or engaging.

The fundamental principal of all scientific observation is accuracy, and no one knew this better than Darwin. No one understood better than he the subtle, treacherous influences that are always at work, distracting, impairing, and distorting exact and lucid vision. There is the danger of seeing what we are accustomed to see and therefore think we see. There is the danger of seeing what others have seen and described before us. There is the supreme danger of seeing what we wish to see, what accords with some preconceived theory or dogma. Against all these dangers Darwin tried to be ever on his guard, and he is constantly warning others of them and emphasizing the importance of pure accuracy and the enormous difficulty of it. 'Good heavens, how difficult accuracy is!'[23] Among all the merits of the scientist he values accuracy highest, the instinct and the ability to record facts correctly: 'I value praise for accurate observation far higher than for any other quality.'[24] And especially in one admirable passage he stresses and reiterates both the difficulty and the value: 'Accuracy is the soul of Natural History. It is hard to become accurate; he who modifies a hair's breadth will never be accurate. . . . Absolute accuracy is the hardest merit to attain, and the highest merit.'[25]

Among the various elements of accuracy, that of statement, as well as of observation, is of course of the utmost importance, yet is too apt to be overlooked. Even those who are careful in their actual observing, may in their report of their observations be much less so. Words are misleading and inadequate things, and the tricks they have played with scientific accuracy have been deplorable. There is the strange ease of mere misstatement. There is the natural tendency to overstate. There is the tendency to clarify verbally what in fact is more or less confused or the opposite difficulty of making verbally clear what the senses may perceive with singular lucidity.

Here again Darwin is constantly on the watch. Memory is misleading and accounts based upon it are apt to be untrustworthy: 'I foolishly trusted to my memory, and was much annoyed to find how hasty and inaccurate many of my remarks were.'[26] Words are inadequate, blundering, they will not render the finer, more delicate shades: 'A difference may be clearly perceived, and yet it may be impossible, at least I have found it so, to state in what the difference consists.'[27] One cannot be too careful, too scrupulous, about one's statements, or too anxious to correct them, when one has made a mistake. And Darwin gets up in the middle of the night and arouses a slumbering friend to explain that, after all, he felt the sense of the sublime more fully in the forests of Brazil than on the top of the Cordilleras.[28]

When one is so mistrustful of one's own records one cannot always accept implicitly the narratives of others. Darwin is eager to get the accounts of other observers, and is singularly deferential to their opinions. At the same time he is gently and watchfully critical, and knows well how to estimate the ability of those with whom he deals. One of the most interesting remarks upon the skill of his methods in obtaining information, and one that every one who reads him carefully will confirm, is Sir William Turner's comment upon 'his care in avoiding leading questions.' [29]

And if Darwin was insistent upon accuracy in records, he was also extraordinarily thorough and exact in mathematical matters and measurement. He speaks of abstract mathematics as having been one of the neglected elements of his education, [30] but he shunned no amount of pains and toil in calculating, wherever he felt it necessary to work out his results. In his books which record the investigation of detail there is an almost incredible amount of slow and careful research involving exact counting and weighing and measuring. 'I was compelled to count under the microscope above 20,000 seeds of *Lythrum salicaria*,' he says casually in one instance, [31] and there are innumerable others of the same kind. In all these calculations the possibility of error haunts him and he does his best to eliminate it, yet still the possibility is there: 'Although I always am endeavoring to be cautious and to mistrust myself, yet I know well how apt I am to make blunders.'[32] If he blundered, what shall be said of some of us? Most interesting and characteristic is the trait, pointed out by his son, that he assumed with singular naïveté the absolute accuracy of the instruments that came to him: 'He had great faith in instruments, and I do not think it naturally occurred to him to doubt the accuracy of a scale or measuring glass.'[33] Yet further, 'it was characteristic of him that he took scrupulous pains in making measurements with his somewhat rough scales.'[34]

As he was exact and particular in calculation and measurement, so he shrank from no amount of detail, did not hesitate to carry his investigations to the last point of minuteness, whenever the full and solid breadth of result demanded it. Apparently nothing escaped him. It was not only what he was looking for, but he noted and seized oddities and exceptions for their larger bearing and for future profit. As his son says, 'A point apparently slight and unconnected with his present work is passed over by many a man almost unconsciously with some half-considered explanation, which is in fact no explanation. It was just these things that he seized on to make a start from.'[35] Thus, on any subject that came up, his memory or his notes

could almost always be appealed to. As Sir Thomas
Farrer puts it, 'What interested me was to see that
on this as on almost any other point of detailed
observation, Mr. Darwin could always say, "Yes,
but at one time I made some observations myself on this particular point; and I think you will
find, etc., etc."'[36]

To appreciate this minuteness and thoroughness,
it is necessary to examine the less known and less
popular books, such as the 'Cross and Self Fertilization' and the 'Different Forms of Flowers.'
In these one is overwhelmed with Darwin's persistence in examining and noting trivial details.
And perhaps most impressive of all is to turn over
the pages of the two immensely solid volumes on
Cirripedes. For many years Darwin devoted himself to the study of these unexciting barnacles,
sometimes wearying, sometimes rebelling, but always keeping at his task until he had completed it.
He himself sometimes wondered whether such prolonged toil at mere description was wholly worth
while; but Huxley believed that the mental discipline was of the greatest possible profit to Darwin's
later work. In any case the exhaustive thoroughness of it is indeed exemplary. How far this goes
may be suggested by one quotation out of many:

THE OBSERVER

I cannot too strongly impress on any one intending to study this class, not to trust to external characters; he must separate and clean and carefully examine the internal structure and form of the compartments and more especially of the opercular valves.'[37] And the examination, in Darwin's case, applied to hundreds of specimens of minute barnacles gathered and sent to him from all parts of the world.

It is hardly necessary to emphasize the enormous amount of labor implied and involved in all these self-imposed tasks of Darwin. Although circumstances compelled him to give a large part of his life to repose, he was by nature a worker. It is true that he sometimes speaks jokingly of his idleness: 'I have been of late shamefully idle, *i.e.*, observing instead of writing, and how much better fun observing is than writing.'[38] But as Huxley well points out, Darwin generally means by idleness 'working hard at something he likes when he ought to be occupied with a less attractive subject.'[39] And Darwin's own more serious comment is, 'I am a pretty man to preach, for I cannot be idle, much as I wish it, and am never comfortable except when at work.'[40] He complains of fatigue, he forces himself to seek recreation, relaxation; but even when his body is at rest, his mind tends to work, refuses to stop working, finds its only real relief in change of occupation and thought.

And as the labor is impressive, so is the patience. The man was naturally nervous, restless, eager. He wanted results, like the rest of us. Yet after he had conceived a theory which he thought destined to subvert the whole realm of science, he waited twenty years for the thorough observation and testing necessary to put the theory into even tentative form. Of all the great scientific qualities perhaps patience is the most essential and the most difficult, and surely patience never had a more supreme exemplar than Charles Darwin. Sometimes even his enduring persistence is temporarily shaken: 'My cirripedial task is an eternal one; I make no perceptible progress. I am sure that they belong to the hour-hand, and I groan under my task.'[41] But though he may groan, he never yields. As his son admirably says of him: 'He used almost to apologize for his patience, saying that he could not bear to be beaten, as if this were rather a sign of weakness on his part. . . . Perseverance seems hardly to express his almost fierce desire to force the truth to reveal itself. He often said that it was important that a man should know the right point at which to give up an inquiry. And I think it was his tendency to pass this point that inclined him to apologize for his perseverance, and gave the air of doggedness to his work.'[42] The intensity of such patience is best appreciated by those who all their lives have scamped and hurried and slighted and touched a thousand things without ever going to the bottom of a single one.

III

Nothing illustrates better the patience of Darwin, and of course also of hundreds of other scientists who are working as he worked in unknown laboratories all over the world, than the process of simple waiting so often necessary to obtain results. Nature demands time, often enormous time, and the brevity of human life and the evanescence of human opportunity mean nothing to her. The careful working out of scientific investigation requires the study of successive generations, sometimes of many, the sowing of the seed and the gathering of the blossom, the close observation of the individual from conception to death, which can be carried on only through long periods of time. The observer must keep a dozen lines of study in his mind, must maintain them side by side, and must be always ready to turn from one to the other, as some new development arises that demands his attention. It was in this phase of long, renewed, continued, enduring watchfulness that Darwin was preëminent. As well appears in his son's record: 'I think it was all due to the vitality and persistence of his mind — a quality I have heard him speak of as if he felt that he was strongly gifted in that respect. Not that he used any such phrases as these about himself, but he would say that he had the power of keeping a subject or question more or less before him for a great many years.'[43] Very little examination of Darwin's books is required to show how amply and constantly this power was exercised.

And to give such patience and taste for continuity their full effect there is needed almost a passion for system, for orderly arrangement, and the habit of putting not only things but thoughts in their proper places, so that they can be called upon at the right moment in the right way. Darwin himself describes his elaborate method of indexing the books that he read and the notes that he made, so that whenever he wished to deal with any special subject, he could turn at once to material bearing upon it: 'Before beginning on any subject

I look to all the short indexes and make a general and classified index, and by taking the one or more proper portfolios I have all the information collected during my life ready for use.' [44]

Such systematic habits of working both demand and imply an orderly and economical use of time. Owing to his limitations of health, Darwin's working time was extremely limited, but he made the most of it. Every usable hour was allotted, and the utmost profit and result were extracted from it. No doubt such sense of pressure is in itself not very beneficial to health, but it means an immense amount of work accomplished. The time was employed thriftily as well as intelligently: 'He saved a great deal of time through not having to do things twice.' [45] And everywhere there is the feeling of the value of minutes which is indicated in Dante's saying,

Chè'l perder tempo, a chi più sa, più spiace. [46]

Or as Darwin himself expresses it: 'A man who dares to waste one hour of time has not discovered the value of life.' [47]

Still another element of observation richly illustrated in Darwin, and closely connected with the patience and the continuity, is the element of comparison. Observation by itself, the mere accumu-

wearing. There was exposure to all sorts of weather, there was the torment of insects, there was endless, inescapable fatigue, which could not be remedied or avoided, but just had to be borne and forgotten in the excitement of great or even little objects to be attained. Glimpses here and there, never unduly emphasized, show what these trials were and how they were met: 'The road, from some recent rain, was full of little puddles of clear water, yet not a drop was drinkable. I had scarcely been twenty hours without water, and only part of the time under a hot sun, yet the thirst rendered me very weak. How people survive two or three days under such circumstances, I cannot imagine.' [51] To put up with discomforts during a camping trip of a few weeks or months is one thing. To endure them constantly for five years implies a very pretty enthusiasm for the cause of science.

Besides these external drawbacks to observation, there are others more subjective and personal. A minor aspect of these has interested me, because it shows such a delightful mixture of human feeling and scientific curiosity. As we shall have occasion to amplify later, Darwin was remarkable for tenderness, for sympathy, for affectionate and kindly interest, not only in humanity generally and in animals, but especially in those directly connected with him. Yet his investigations of expression led him, forced him, to a calm and cold-blooded analysis of situations and emotions which at the same time made the strongest appeal to his sympathies. All through his children's infancy he pursued the practice of making notes on them, yet it is most curious to trace the play of personal emotion in combination with the abstract research, and the working of this well appears in his son's remark: 'It was characteristic of him that (as I have heard him tell), although he was so anxious to observe the expression of a crying child, his sympathy with the grief spoiled his observation.'[52] A more impersonal example is his careful record as to a woman whom he studied in a railway carriage, watching with minute attention the movement of her *depressores anguli oris*, which appeared to indicate extreme distress: 'As her countenance remained as placid as ever, I reflected how meaningless was this contraction, and how easily one might be deceived. The thought had hardly occurred to me when I saw that her eyes suddenly became suffused with tears almost to overflowing and her whole countenance fell. There could now be no doubt that some painful recollection, perhaps that of a long-lost child, was passing through her mind.' [53] And so instances of intense individual suffering became generalized into typical cases of scientific record.

Far more important, however, in Darwin's career, as a drawback to scientific observation, than any intrusions of subjective sympathy, were the bitter, persistent limitations of physical illness and weakness. During a very large part of his life he was tormented by nervous indigestion, manifesting itself, under any strain, in persistent nausea. This first appeared in the ever-returning and unconquerable sea-sickness which made all his southern voyages a misery. When the ocean was at all boisterous the malady prostrated him, and those who know how absolutely prostrating sea-sickness is will appreciate the positive heroism which enabled him to prosecute his journey and his researches with such a handicap.

After his return to England the trouble continued to hound and haunt him through all his later years. He never could work for more than a small portion of the day. The excitement of visitors always upset him. There were long periods when any work was impossible and often an absorbing investigation had to be laid aside altogether just at the most critical point, laid aside so completely that not only actual labor but even thought was prohibited. The idleness which he detested was forced upon him for a very large part of his days and hours and the spirit framed for such constant and intense activity was obliged to discipline itself to the most irksome and profitless repose.

It made no difference in the intensity or the persistence of his scientific preoccupations. Perhaps if he had abandoned his pursuits altogether and had contented himself with an indolent and externally diversified existence, he might have enjoyed reasonable health. But he would not yield for a moment. His whole soul was in the studies, the pursuits, the investigations that enthralled and inspired him, and life without them would have been inconceivable. 'We have come here for rest for me, which I have much needed; and shall remain here for about ten days more, and then home to work, which is my sole pleasure in life.'[54] That is the constant note. In the midst of his travels he wrote home: 'My mind has been since leaving England, in a perfect *hurricane* of delight and astonishment, and to this hour scarcely a minute has passed in idleness.'[55] The body might lag and drag and harass and torment, but the spirit lived in just such a hurricane of excitement and enthusiasm always.

IV

It must be recognized that even in the pure habit of observation for itself, whether in the natural world or otherwise, there is a charm for those who are born for it. Curiosity is a natural instinct with most of us, and there is inexhaustible entertainment in letting the spirit lie fallow within, while the external world plays upon it with an endless succession of picturesque incidents and highly colored circumstance. At the same time, and especially in the realm of nature, it is astonishing what a difference even a little knowledge makes. Most of us walk through the fields and woods like blind men, utterly oblivious of all the fascinating secrets which await our eyes and ears if we were only alive to them. As one who has always delighted in solitary wood walks merely for their associative beauty, I at least can bewail the deplorable ignorance as to plants and birds and insects which makes it impossible for me even to interrogate them intelligently. Lack of time or natural indolence have prevented my accumulating the knowledge which would put all these things in their proper relations and make them tell a story which the trained and expert observer instantly and instinctively reads in them. It is comforting to find even Darwin complaining of the same ignorance and the same blindness, when he gets into surroundings that are strange to him. Thus in his earlier voyaging, he notes: 'One great source of perplexity to me is an utter ignorance whether I note the right facts, and whether they are of sufficient importance to interest others.'[56] And again even more vividly: 'It is positively distressing to walk in the glorious forest amidst such treasures and feel they are all thrown away upon one.'[57]

Then with the coming of a little knowledge the observation is enriched, transfigured, glorified. Hear what Thoreau says of even the apparently dry and profitless acquisition of nomenclature: 'With the knowledge of the name comes a distincter recognition and knowledge of the thing. That shore is now more describable and poetic even. My knowledge was cramped and confined before, and grew rusty because not used — for it could not be used. My knowledge now becomes communicable and grows by communication.'[58] Knowledge in one branch amplifies and steadies observation in that branch. Knowledge of many branches connects them and makes each one throw light on all the others. Record of others' observations or of your own through several years give each new year double significance and fruitfulness. As Thoreau again puts it: 'I soon found myself observing when plants first blossomed and leafed, and I followed it up early and late, far and near, several years in succession, running to different sides of the town and into the neighboring towns, often between twenty and thirty miles in a day.' [59] If your attention gets fixed upon some special point to be elucidated, every walk you take, and almost every step brings out some development which you did not consider or imagine before. In short the enrichment of knowledge doubles, triples, quintuples your vision, since it teaches you what to look for, and even while it sometimes betrays, teaches you what to see.

But if mere general scientific knowledge is so stimulating and so enlarging in the realm of observation, how infinitely more fruitful is the Darwinian view of the interrelated development of all life including that of man. Whatever may be said, whatever we may have to say later, of the injurious action of this view upon the status of man himself, there can be no question as to the transforming, magical effect of it upon the study of the natural world. Before the evolutionary attitude, the observation of plants and animals was at best a mere gratification of curiosity. The proper study of mankind was man, and the investigation of birds and insects was only distraction and diversion. But the instant it appeared that all the threads of life were intertwined and that in disentangling even the slightest of them you might be getting the clue to the riddle of the whole, all was changed. When it comes to be felt that the history of man, of his instincts, of his passions, of his powers, of his future, of his fate, is written in his past, and that past is to be studied, if at all, in the history of the humblest creatures who are animated by the same mysterious impulse of life that moulds and governs him, the interest of natural observation is increased a thousandfold. It is not exaggerating to say that the study of natural history is an entirely different pursuit since Darwin from what it was before.

It is evident that Darwin himself was constantly and immensely impressed by the profound significance thus added to scientific research. A passage in his earlier note-books shows how the idea was beginning to take hold of him: 'If we choose to let conjecture run wild, then animals, our fellow brethren in pain, disease, death, suffering and famine — our slaves in the most laborious works, our companions in our amusements — they may partake of our origin in one common ancestor — we may be all melted together.'[60]

A striking concrete illustration of the community of life, even in the humblest forms, appears in the book on earth-worms and suggests Emerson's poetical version of the same idea,

'And striving to be man the worm
Mounts through all the spires of form:'

'It may be well to remember how perfect the sense of touch becomes in a man when born blind and deaf, as are worms. If worms have the power of acquiring some notion, however rude, of the shape of an object and of their burrows, as seems to be the case, they deserve to be called intelligent; for they then act in nearly the same manner as would a man under similar circumstances.'[61] While a celebrated passage in 'The Origin of Species' develops the idea abstractly, by implication at least placing man at the apex of the whole: 'As buds give rise by growth to fresh buds, and these, if vigorous, branch out and overtop on all sides many a feebler branch, so by generation I believe it has been with the great Tree of Life, which fills with its dead and broken branches the crust of the earth, and covers the surface with its ever-branching and beautiful ramifications.'[62]

THE OBSERVER

Wallace said of his great friend and competitor, 'Again, both Darwin and myself had what he terms "the mere passion of collecting"... I should describe it rather as an intense interest in the mere *variety* of living things.'[63] The simple observer is carried away, absorbed, ravished by the delight and the fascinating play of this variety of living things, but how far more absorbing and inexhaustible does the delight become when we feel that in studying this universal play of life we are every moment probing the depths of our own souls.

CHAPTER II
DARWIN: THE THINKER
I

MERE observation of the natural world, varied, fascinating, inexhaustible as it is, affords only the material for science. Observed facts must be built up, woven together, ordered, arranged, systematized into conclusions and theories by reflection and reason, if they are to have full bearing on life and the universe. Knowledge is the accumulation of facts. Wisdom is the establishment of relations. And just because the latter process is delicate and perilous, it is all the more delightful. The lofty scorn of the true philosopher for mere perception is well shown in Royer Collard's remark: 'There is nothing so despicable as a fact.' Which does not prevent philosophers or any one else from making facts the essential basis of all discussion of relations. Darwin's own comments on the general connection between the two are always interesting: 'I have an old belief that a good observer really means a good theorist,'[1] and again: 'About thirty years ago there was much talk that geologists ought only to ob-

DOWN HOUSE FROM THE GARDEN

serve and not theorize; and I well remember some one saying that at this rate a man might as well go into a gravel-pit and count the pebbles and describe the colors. How odd it is that any one should not see that all observation must be for or against some view if it is to be of any service.'[2]

It is supposed to be one of the chief functions of education to develop this faculty of relating facts to each other and to train and strengthen the reasoning powers. Darwin did not feel that education did much for him in this line, at any rate in the scientific directions which were of especial interest to him. He believed that his academic discipline was largely wasted. Making Latin verses did not appeal. More general lines of current information attracted him very little, and he seemed at times oddly ignorant of what the ordinary educated man is expected to know. Thus his son records that he once asked Hooker where 'this place Wien is where they publish so many books.'[3] He read vastly in all that concerned his own work, but that very fact prevented his keeping up with daily interests that were remote from it. His own comment on his university experience is bitter: 'During the three years which I spent at Cambridge my time was wasted, as far as the academical studies were concerned, as completely as at Edinburgh and at school.'⁴ And he believed that he had learned everything that to him was worth learning pretty much by his own efforts: 'I consider that all I have learnt of any value has been self-taught.'⁵

With this sort of discipline behind him, it is of great interest to examine his general attitude toward the connection of reasoning and fact. To some of us the controversy between induction and deduction has always seemed rather profitless. The Baconian insistence upon the absolute necessity of fact as the basis of all solid theory is of course indisputably just. But to talk of proceeding from abstract theory to the investigation of fact seems as barren as to wander aimlessly in unassorted realms of fact without the assistance of theory. It is comforting, therefore, to find so clear and systematic a thinker as Huxley unwilling to identify his processes with either complete induction or deduction: 'Those who refuse to go beyond fact rarely get as far as fact; and any one who has studied the history of science knows that almost every great step therein has been made by the "anticipation of nature," that is, by the invention of hypotheses which, though verifiable, often had very little foundation to start with; and not unfrequently, in spite of a long career of usefulness, turned out to be wholly erroneous in the long run.'[6]

Now Darwin obviously finds himself in precisely the uncertainty between inductive and deductive methods that Huxley here indicates. His instincts were naturally hostile to abstract theory, which used facts as playthings to substantiate soaring conjecture. He says in regard to one scientific author: 'I am not convinced, partly I think owing to the deductive cast of much of his reasoning; and. I know not why, but I never feel convinced by deduction, even in the case of H. Spencer's writings.'[7] And he speaks even more specifically concerning Spencer himself: 'I always feel a malicious pleasure when *a priori* conclusions are knocked on the head; and therefore I felt somewhat like a devil when I read your remarks on Herbert Spencer.'[8] Early and late he emphasized that 'no one has a right to speculate without distinct facts.'[9] Yet at the same time he urges and reiterates that the mere collection of facts, without some basis of theory for guidance and elucidation, is foolish and profitless: 'I am a firm believer that without speculation there is no good and original observation.'[10]

The truth is, the importance of imaginative power in the equipment of a great scientist is often underestimated. Exact and watchful vision is the first necessity; but it does not go far, or not farthest, except as it has behind it the thoughts that wander through eternity, the vast and questing genius that is perpetually on the lookout for causes and explanations and is eager to evolve theory from the sure and substantial but inanimate basis of fact. Even Thoreau almost deplores his intense pre-occupation with the fascinating business of observing: 'Man cannot afford to be a naturalist, to look at Nature directly, but only with the side of his eye. He must look through and beyond her. To look at her is fatal as to look at the head of Medusa. It turns the man of science to stone. I feel that I am dissipated by so many observations. . . . I have almost a slight, dry headache as the result of all this observing.'[11] Theory, speculation, must be perpetually checked and restrained by the precision of systematic logic, but the accurate eye and the careful finger need to be supplemented by the eternally active mind.

As to the activity of Darwin's mind there can be no question whatever. He not only saw, but he thought incessantly. If you compare the Beagle Journal with the Journal of Thoreau, you see at once how much more quick and ready the English naturalist is with speculation and conjecture. The smallest fact is apt to set him off on a train of theory, where Thoreau simply records, or possibly compares, and passes on. How significant is the brief comment of Asa Gray, in regard to some botanical point which as a specialist in that line he should have been the first to develop: 'That is real Darwin. I just wonder you and I never thought of it. But *he* did.' [12] And he not only thought himself, he had the rarer and more valuable faculty of making others think. His mind was so intense and so magnetic in its constant activity that all those who came into contact with it were impelled and fired to work double on speculation of their own. 'You stimulate my mind,' says Gray again, 'far more than any one else, except, perhaps Hooker.' [13]

On this point of intellectual fertility, as on his other scientific qualifications, it is most interesting to hear Darwin himself. The mental activity was present early and late, and it does not appear that the exuberance of youth especially emphasized it or that it tended to increase with the later desire to develop and elaborate his special theories. He himself says in the Autobiographical sketch: 'I am not conscious of any change in my mind during the last thirty years, excepting in one point:...

I think that I have become a little more skillful in guessing right explanations and in devising experimental tests; but this may probably be the result of mere practice, and of a larger store of knowledge.' [14]

The quick intelligence was always working, sometimes wearily, sometimes eagerly, but working, unless absolute physical prostration forbade. When he is too exhausted, he complains: 'Facts compel me to conclude that my brain was never formed for much thinking.' [15] But if so, he certainly lived contrary to his nature. He tells us that he cannot resist forming hypotheses on every subject.[16] Sometimes he bewails the tendency, realizing its drawbacks and dangers. Sometimes he gives way to it, recognizing its charm: 'It is delightful to have many points fermenting in one's brain.' [17] Speculation is fascinating. Theory gives form and texture to the fleeting drift and confusion of fact. Yet even when one indulges with most enthusiasm, a touch of humor shows that the satisfaction must be tempered with a certain lack of entire confidence: 'That is a splendid fact about the white moths; it warms one's very blood to see a theory thus almost proved to be true.' [18]

For the wonder and the interest of Darwin is, that, with such an eager and perpetual bent toward theorizing, he could keep the bent so fully under control. As Karl Pearson puts it, generally: 'Hundreds of men have allowed their imagination to solve the universe, but the men who have contributed to our real understanding of natural phenomena have been those who were unstinted in their application of criticism to the product of their imaginations.' [19] Surely no man applied such criticism more carefully, more conscientiously, more constantly than Darwin. He analyzes his own position and sees the dangers of it: 'Living so solitary as I do, one gets to think in a silly manner of one's own work.' [20] He sees constantly how theory interferes and warps the judgment: 'I have not a doubt that before many months are over I shall be longing for the most dishonest species as being more honest than the honestest theories.' [21] The possibility of error haunts him, torments him, and he knows well how apt his own speculative disposition is to mislead: 'What you hint at generally is very, very true: that my work will be grievously hypothetical, and large parts by no means worthy of being called induction, my commonest error being probably induction from too few facts.' [22] As a consequence he was ever on his guard against being led astray. The tempting little demon of hypothesis might be

luring round the corner: 'It is as difficult not to
form some opinion as it is to form a correct judgment.' [23] But whatever opinion was formed must be
corrected, must be adjusted, must be tested, by the
cold and rigid measure of fact. As he says himself,
'I have steadily endeavored to keep my mind free
so as to give up any hypothesis, however much beloved (and I cannot resist forming one on every
subject), as soon as the facts are shown to be opposed to it.' [24] And one who knew him well and had
studied him carefully says the same thing with
equal emphasis: 'His long experience had given
him a kind of instinctive insight into the method of
attack of any biological problem, however unfam-
iliar to him, while he rigidly controlled the fertility of his mind in hypothetical explanations by the
no less fertility of ingeniously devised experiment.' [25]

In regard to this matter of speculative freedom
and the tendency to let imagination run wild, it
is interesting to watch Darwin's comments on the
general methods of others. The excess of ab-
stinence he indeed deplores, recognizing that a
man's extreme caution may prevent him from
theorizing enough: 'How many astronomers have
labored their whole lives on observations, and have

not drawn a single conclusion.'[26] But the danger on the other side is so great and so ruinous that it cannot be enough insisted on, and indeed at times it makes all generalization suspicious and almost a thing to be eschewed: 'I look at a strong tendency to generalize as an entire evil.'[27] At any rate, the theorist must never forget the subjective element, that his preconceptions and prejudices are apt to warp his judgment and distort his vision, till the keenest of observers and the sanest of thinkers may go astray: 'the firmest conviction of the truth of a doctrine by its author seems, alas, not to be the slightest guarantee of truth.'[28]

The profit and the lesson of all which must be constantly borne home to oneself: 'When I think of the many cases of men who have studied one subject for years, and have persuaded themselves of the truth of the foolishest doctrines, I feel sometimes a little frightened, whether I may not be one of these monomaniacs.'[29]

To appreciate fully Darwin's combination of mental activity and fertility with moderation and restraint, it is well to place him between two extreme types of thinkers. On the one hand, there is the born essential reasoner, and logician, Spinoza, for instance, or Hegel, or Darwin's own contemporary, Spencer, the man who to a greater or less extent takes fact for his foundation, but who by nature and temperament delights to weave an elaborate web of logical theory, rigid and perfect in its appearance of systematic deduction, but too apt in the end to treat facts with indifference if not disrespect. I like especially in this regard to compare Darwin with Lucretius. The *De Rerum Natura* is one of the most striking, enthralling examples of what I should call passionate thinking. Theoretical problems take hold of Lucretius like the ecstasies of love. He tears and wrenches at the roots of thought, determined to make them yield to the delving vigor of his eager search. Now Darwin has a broad and constant curiosity, his interest may well be called enthusiasm, and he himself uses the term passion for it: 'Hence it has come to be a passion with me to try to connect all such facts by some sort of hypothesis.'[30] Yet in no phase of his nature should I be inclined ever to employ the general word, 'passion,' and it seems to me that every page of Lucretius is stamped with a devouring ardor different from anything Darwin knew.

On the other hand, over against these furious reasoners, I should set Darwin's close contemporary, Sainte-Beuve, who, as I said in the previous chapter was, in some aspects, as admirable a representative of the scientific spirit as Darwin himself. The endless curiosity, the unlimited observation of fact, as embodied in the human subject, have never been more richly exemplified than in the great French critic. But Sainte-Beuve was no reasoner in the larger sense. He did not even avoid reasoning from mistrust: he had no taste for it, and when he dealt with it, it was always charily and with extreme reserve. He delighted to study and portray individuals and to allow those individuals, as it were, to classify themselves and so to point the way to general results.

Between these two extremes Darwin stands, as one who used reasoning to the fullest extent for the interpretation of fact, yet at the same time always stuck closely and rigidly to the fact itself, and would not allow it to be for an instant distorted by the reasoning process.

II

The supreme means for keeping theory on a basis of fact is of course unfailing, persistent, ever-varied experiment. In the preceding chapter we have seen observation lead naturally to experiment; but experiment is observation guided, directed, and illuminated by theory. And assuredly no scientist ever had the love and the habit of experiment more firmly fixed than Darwin. The explanation of phenomena was all very well in its place, essential, absorbing, but he would have agreed absolutely with Aristotle as to the proper ordering of the process: 'After this we shall pass on to the discussion of causes. For to do this when the investigation of the details is complete, is the proper and natural method, and that whereby the subject and the premises of our argument will afterwards be rendered plain.'[31] The fascination of experiment in itself was endless and almost sufficing: 'The love of experiment was very strong in him,' says his son, 'and I can remember the way he would say, "I shan't be easy till I have tried it," as if an outside force were driving him.'[32] There was a sense of adventure about it, of discovery, and he loved to try things that seemed almost fantastic and absurd: 'If you knew some of the experiments (if they may be so-called) which I am trying, you would have a good right to sneer, for they are so *absurd* even in *my* opinion that I dare not tell you.'[33] And more concisely and vividly: 'I am like a gambler and love a wild experiment.'[34] The best comment on which is the excellent remark of Professor

Castle: 'Most advances in practical affairs are made by those who have the courage to attempt what others *with good reason think unattainable*. When such attempts have succeeded, the world simply revises its classification of things attainable and unattainable, and makes a fresh start.'[35]

The first thing in regard to experiment is conditions. There are of course rough and elementary experiments, involving only simple principles, which do not require minute care in detail. But in many cases the nicest and most delicate preparation and adjustment are indispensable to ensure reliable results. The extensive equipment of modern laboratories was not at Darwin's command, and though he had considerable financial resources, he could not afford the unlimited outlay of commercial research. Thus, we read of one of Mr. Burbank's trials: 'Forty thousand blackberry and raspberry hybrids were produced and grown until the fruit matured. Then from the whole lot a single variety was chosen as the best. . . . All others were uprooted with their crop of ripening berries, heaped up into a pile twelve feet wide, fourteen feet high, and twenty-two feet long, and burned. Nothing remained of this expensive and lengthy experiment, except the one parent plant of the new variety.'[36]

Darwin could hardly work on any such elaborate scale as this. Yet, as one turns over his vast record of experiment, one is astonished to see how thorough and painstaking was his effort to avoid accidents and to provide for disturbing contingencies. Take, for instance, as a minor but significant illustration, his account of the difficulty in carrying out the specific fertilization of certain plants: 'In making eighteen different unions, sometimes on windy days, and pestered by bees and flies buzzing about, some few errors could hardly be avoided. One day I had to keep a third man by me all the time to prevent the bees visiting the uncovered plants, for in a few seconds' time they might have done irreparable mischief. It was also extremely difficult to exclude minute Diptera from the net.'[37]

Another vital consideration as to experiment, is that it should be kept impersonal. In most cases, if one is to experiment fruitfully and satisfactorily, there should be some special object in view, some particular point to be rejected or confirmed. Unless you know just what you are looking for, you are apt not to see. Again and again in Darwin's book on Orchids, as in many of the others, we read that he made investigations and got no results, simply because he did not have in mind theoretical possibilities. When he had reasoned out what ought to happen or might happen, he often found that it did. The danger of this method is obvious. When the experimenter is so desperately anxious to see something, unless he is most carefully trained and disciplined, he will see it. It is not to be supposed that Darwin always escaped this danger, but few men have been more prepared for it or more ready to allow for it than he. His confession of prejudice, his recognition of the importance of certain points in his general theory and of his unwillingness to have anything interfere with them are among his greatest charms: 'I remember well the time when the thought of the eye made me cold all over. . . . The sight of a feather in a peacock's tail, whenever I gaze at it, makes me sick.' [38]

We have already enlarged under observation on the essential quality of accuracy, and it may simply be added that accuracy is doubly important in all experiments for a theoretical purpose. Accuracy, complete, detailed, mathematical exactitude, was Darwin's hobby, and the minuteness of his record constantly exemplifies it.

Also, to confirm their accuracy experiments have to be repeated. Goethe remarks with justice that it is not necessary to travel all over the world to make sure that the sky is everywhere blue,[39] and no doubt there are repetitions that are vain and superfluous. But many difficult and delicate researches have to be gone over again and again that the minutest detail may be complete; and the process may involve months of tedious delay. Darwin's unfailing care, both to repeat and to avoid repetition, is well indicated in his son's comment: 'Although he would patiently go on repeating experiments where there was any good to be gained, he could not endure having to repeat an experiment which ought, if complete care had been taken, to have succeeded the first time.' [40] Here too, one cannot appreciate how immense and thorough his experimentation was without looking through such books as the 'Animals and Plants under Domestication' or 'The Power of Movement in Plants.' The endless repetition of slightly varied combinations to test a difficult or remote conclusion makes one feel how persistent and inexhaustible the patience was. And after all the years of repeated and varied research and investigation he writes the almost pathetic epilogue six months before his death: 'I wish that I had enough strength and spirit to commence a fresh set of experiments, and publish the results, with a full recantation of my errors when convinced of them.' [41]

Finally, experiments have to be not only made, but recorded, and the accuracy, so essential with all scientific observation, is above all essential here, since the omission of a link in the record may be ruinous to the continuity of the logical chain. It is peculiarly characteristic of Darwin that he wanted the record of error and mistake as well as of success. 'I remember,' says his son, 'how strongly he urged the necessity of keeping the notes of experiments which failed, and to this rule he always adhered.' [42] The value of preserving and comparing apparently insignificant and meaningless notes is sometimes brought out, as in a special case of orchids: 'I had given up the case as hopeless, until summing up my observations, the explanation presently to be given, and subsequently proved by repeated experiments to be correct, suddenly occurred to me.' [43] Long experience of his own mistakes and failures induces extreme scepticism as to the results of others: '*The difficulty is to know what to trust.*' [44] Even when he has taken the greatest pains, the scepticism often lingers and forces him to repeat although with an identical result: 'Notwithstanding the care taken and the number of trials made, when in the following year I looked merely at the results, without reading over my observations, I again thought that there must have been some error, and thirty-five fresh trials were made with the weakest solution; but the results were as plainly marked as before.'[45] And thus the long series of packed, closely printed volumes forms an amazing record of a life of zealous, persistent, curious experimentation from beginning to end.

III

Now let us look a little more closely at the stuff and quality of Darwin's logical processes, considered as such. He himself often complains of the slowness and difficulty of his thinking. It is hard for him to arrange his thoughts, he says, hard for him to get them into the lucid and effective order which carries conviction with it, almost enforces conviction by the power of its own movement. He says of one of his critics: 'He admits to a certain extent Natural Selection, yet I am sure does not understand me. It is strange that very few do, and I am become quite convinced that I must be an extremely bad explainer.'[46]

It is worth while to note the comments of Huxley, as one of Darwin's staunchest friends and supporters, on his reasoning faculty and processes. When Romanes lauds Darwin's colossal intellect, Huxley is inclined to protest: 'Colossal does not seem to me to be the right epithet for Darwin's intellect. He had a clear, rapid intelligence, a great memory, a vivid imagination, and what made his greatness was the strict subordination of all these to the love of truth.' [47] Elsewhere Huxley adds: 'Exposition was not Darwin's forte — and his English is sometimes wonderful. But there is a marvelous dumb sagacity about him and he gets to truth by ways as dark as those of the Heathen Chinee.' [48] Of 'The Origin of Species' Huxley writes: 'It is one of the hardest books to understand thoroughly that I know of.' [49] And again, more amply: 'Long occupation with the work has led the present writer to believe that "The Origin of Species" is one of the hardest of books to master, and he is justified in this conviction by observing that although the "Origin" has been close on thirty years before the world, the strangest misconceptions of the essential nature of the theory therein advocated are still put forth by serious writers.' [50] Critics less friendly to Darwin than Huxley have spoken still more strongly.

I feel that Huxley's judgment is too severe. It

is true that Darwin had not the admirable gift of logical, lucid exposition which made Huxley himself one of the most luminous of scientific writers. But even when Darwin's reasoning is most complex and difficult, there is a notable quality of sincerity and single-mindedness, which wins and retains your confidence. He seems somehow to have an exceptional power of taking you into his mental processes, and to make you think and see and feel as he does. If you feel that he may be wrong, it is because he feels that he may be wrong himself.

It is profitable to examine a little more in detail some illustrations of Darwin's scientific theorizing. The great central doctrine of evolution, with its buttressing support of natural selection, will fill our next chapter, but there are several lesser developments of speculation which deserve notice. I need hardly say that we are not in any way discussing the validity of the theories in the abstract, but simply Darwin's fashion of framing, holding, and sustaining them.

There is first the theory as to the formation of coral reefs. At an early period in his career Darwin conceived the idea that these reefs were produced by the subsidence of the ocean bed and the steady building up of the coral insects toward the surface. He himself admits that this theory was the most deductive of all that he ever urged and the least founded in the beginning upon a wide and careful investigation of fact. Alexander Agassiz, who, after extensive research, was not disposed to accept it, wrote: 'Darwin's observations were all theoretical, based upon chartographic study in his house, a very poor way of doing, and that's the way all his coral reef work has been done.' [51] And the theory has met with strenuous opposition from many quarters, though one critic says in regard to it: 'Be it true or not, be it a competent explanation or not, no matter. In influence on geology it has been as far-reaching as the doctrine of natural selection has been on biology.' [52] But Darwin himself clung to it to the end, meeting objections with vast ingenuity and reiterating his positions with ampler and more penetrating arguments. Yet through all the persistence there is the readiness at any moment to see the other side. 'I must still adhere to my opinion, that the atolls and barrier reefs in the middle of the Pacific and Indian Oceans indicate subsidence, but I fully agree with you that such cases as that of the Pellew Islands, if of at all frequent occurrence, would make my general conclusions of very little value. Future observers must decide between us.' [53] And he writes frankly to Alexander Agassiz: 'If I am wrong, the sooner I am knocked on the head and annihilated so much the better.' [54]

Another instance of Darwin's zeal and ingenuity in reasoning is the theory of sexual selection, devised to meet some difficulties in his general argument. Many animals have certain so-called secondary sexual characteristics, that is, characteristics affecting one sex only yet not directly involved in the reproductive process. Darwin believed that these characteristics were largely developed through the working of natural selection upon the basis of the preference of one sex for individuals of the other for mating purposes. That is to say, the splendor of the male peacock's tail made him more attractive to the female and therefore more successful with her. There were numerous and obvious difficulties in this view, as the assumption of a fine æsthetic sense in comparatively lowly organized creatures, and it was energetically disputed from the start. Wallace, Darwin's ardent fellow-thinker and coadjutor, was anything but favorable to it. Yet Darwin's faith was never really shaken. He persisted to the end, making new experiments and investigations, and meeting his adversaries'

contentions with vast and varied resource. In
'The Descent of Man' he wrote: 'For my own
part I conclude that of all the causes which have
led to the differences in external appearance between the races of man, and to a certain extent
between man and the lower animals, sexual selection
has been the most efficient.' [55] Nevertheless, it is
fascinating to see him reveal the doubt and the
questioning that were inwrought with conviction
in his mind. He writes to Wallace: 'I grieve to
differ from you, and it actually terrifies me and
makes me constantly distrust myself.' [56] Again:
'You will be pleased to hear that I am undergoing
severe distress about protection and sexual selection; this morning I oscillated with joy towards
you; this evening I have swung back to my [old] position, out of which I fear I shall never get.' [57] And
he sums up the process with a general remark of
the largest and most fruitful bearing: 'I sometimes marvel how truth progresses, so difficult is it
for one man to convince another, unless his mind is
vacant. Nevertheless, I myself to a certain extent
contradict my own remark, for I believe far more
in the importance of protection than I did before
reading your articles.' [58]

Still another example of theorizing is the doctrine of pangenesis. Darwin's general theory of evolution which dealt so much with heredity, was closely complicated with the difficulty of understanding how one minute reproductive cell could transmit by inheritance all the complicated variety of organs and functions in a highly developed plant or animal. To meet this difficulty he devised the explanation of pangenesis (he doubts about the name, because 'my wife says it sounds wicked, like pantheism'),[59] that is, the idea that the primitive cell contains a great number of *gemmules*, each transmitting and originating some particular organ with its varied functions. Here again the theory, as Darwin conceived it, did not find general acceptance, though in some respects it surprisingly anticipates the results of the latest modern research. But the interesting thing is to see the ardor with which its inventor worked it out and the elaborate argument with which he carries it through the latter part of the great work on 'Animals and Plants under Domestication.' It is difficult, he admits. He does not blame any one for disputing it, or for rejecting it, or even for laughing at it. 'The hypothesis of Pangenesis, as applied to the several great classes of facts just discussed, no doubt is extremely complex, but so are the facts.'[60]

And then he lets his imagination range more widely than usual in contemplating possible deductions and consequences: 'No other attempt, as far as I am aware, has been made, imperfect as this confessedly is, to connect under one point of view these several grand classes of facts. An organic being is a microcosm — a little universe, formed of a host of self-propagating organisms, inconceivably minute and numerous as the stars in heaven.'[61] Yet here again he introduces the inevitable reservation and in his Autobiographical Sketch he says: 'Towards the end of the work I give my well-abused hypothesis of Pangenesis. An unverified hypothesis is of little or no value; but if any one should hereafter be led to make observations by which some such hypothesis could be established, I shall have done good service.'[62]

It seems sometimes surprising that, with this marked bent towards abstract speculation, which it was so difficult to control, Darwin should have been always so indifferent to philosophical thought on the ultimate questions of the universe. He admits that he knew little of metaphysics and cared little for them. But this again is instructive as to the peculiar balance of his temperament. He liked to speculate, but he would not speculate for a moment without a firm foundation of fact. His feet must be based first on the solid tangible earth. Then if his head would not reach the clouds, he would keep out of them.

IV

It will be profitable to consider more in detail some specific elements of Darwin's reasoning. In the first place, we have seen everywhere and in all connections that his propensity to eager theorizing was tempered with an unfailing sense of doubt and mistrust. He was indeed always disposed to act in the spirit of Weisman's remark: 'When we are confronted with facts which we see no possibility of understanding save on a single hypothesis, even though it be an undemonstratable one, we are naturally led to accept the hypothesis, at least until a better one can be found.' [63] And he recognized fully the force of the comment which Huxley makes on a phrase of Goethe, to the effect that doubt must not be blighting or destructive, but fruitful and stimulating: 'Goethe has an excellent aphorism defining that state of mind which he calls "*Thätige Skepsis*" — active doubt. It is doubt which so loves truth that it neither dares rest in doubting nor extinguish itself by unjustified belief.' [64]

At the same time, the doubt was there, was temperamental, and could not be altogether extinguished, even when the rush of the logical impetus was fullest. One beautiful expression of it among many is, 'When you say you cannot master the train of thoughts, I know well enough that they are too doubtful and obscure to be mastered. I have often experienced what you call the humiliating feeling of getting more and more involved in doubt the more one thinks of the facts and reasoning on doubtful points.'[65] The truth is, that Darwin had in a high degree the quality, often so hampering to the man of practical action, but invaluable to the thinker, of getting outside of himself and his own point of view and criticizing it as if it were the standpoint of some one else. He himself indicates this forcibly in connection with returning to one's ideas after an interval: 'The delay in this case, as with all my other books, has been a great advantage to me; for a man after a long interval can criticize his own work, almost as well as if it were that of another person.'[66] Some men can.

Another characteristic of Darwin's mental processes is his way of meeting difficulties. The born reasoner is apt to slur over obstacles and objections, to devote himself with endless ingenuity to eliminating them rather than facing them squarely. Darwin was ingenious enough, but he did not dodge difficulties. Instead of doing so, his propensity was, if anything, to make them and seek them. It was said of Pasteur, so like Darwin in many points: 'No adversary of M. Pasteur had formulated this argument; but M. Pasteur, who had within himself an ever-present adversary, always on the watch and determined to yield only to the force of accumulated evidence, himself raised the objection.'[67] So Darwin. As he himself records, and no thinker ever laid down a more significant principle or one more revealing for his own mental constitution: 'I had, also, during many years followed a golden rule, namely, that whenever a published fact, a new observation or thought came across me, which was opposed to my general results, to make a memorandum of it without fail and at once; for I had found by experience that such facts and thoughts were far more apt to escape from the memory than favorable ones.'[68] And the intense consciousness of objections and difficulties appears even more vividly in the sentence: 'I cannot too strongly express my conviction of the general truth of my doctrines, and God knows I have never shirked a difficulty.'[69]

THE THINKER

The recognition of obstacles and complications constantly popping up from everywhere naturally necessitated endless revision and recasting. Here again, the habitual reasoner, having once set his mould is reluctant to alter it. Not so Darwin. There are indeed times when even he rebels and declares that it will be more fruitful to follow new paths than to be perpetually adjusting the old. But in general his readiness to alter and reconstruct is unlimited. He revises and works over his books. In doing so he showed his characteristic disposition to accept and defer to the judgment of others. How charming is his daughter's account of this: 'He was always so ready to be convinced that any suggested alteration was an improvement, and so full of gratitude for the trouble taken. I do not think that he ever used to forget to tell me what improvement he thought that I had made, and he used almost to excuse himself if he did not agree with any correction. I think I felt the singular modesty and graciousness of his nature through thus working for him in a way I never should otherwise have done.' [70] There is no better way to appreciate the extent and the persistence of Darwin's revision than to make even a cursory comparison of the first and the last editions of the 'Origin.'

73

Almost every page shows minor or considerable changes, and while some are no doubt mere matters of language, many have a bearing, however slight, on the trend of the reasoning, deepening, or strengthening, or clarifying it.

It is profitable also to watch Darwin's attitude towards argument, the direct interchange of view by those who take different sides of a case and are at once eager to advance their own and to detect the flaws in their opponent's. It is very evident that he was not a quick and natural arguer, as was Huxley, for instance. His son says: 'He used to say of himself that he was not quick enough to hold an argument with any one, and I think this was true. Unless it was a subject on which he was just then at work, he could not get the train of argument into working order quickly enough.'[71] And Darwin confesses the same thing with his unfailing, charming naïveté, in a letter to Hooker: 'I am astonished at your success and audacity. It is something unintelligible to me how any one can argue in public like orators do. I had no idea you had this power.'[72]

Arguments haunted him, agitated him, disturbed him. Active discussion was apt to be followed by a broken night, filled with the things that might and should have been said and were not. Even of a conversation quite remote from his scientific interest he says: 'Your slave discussion disturbed me much; but as you would care no more for my opinion on this head than for the ashes of this letter, I will say nothing except that it gave me some sleepless, most uncomfortable hours.' [73]

The gift I have before suggested, of getting outside of your own position and judging it as another would, while it benefits the results of argument, is most hampering in the process, since one finds oneself stating one's adversary's case sometimes more forcibly than he does himself. Darwin often repeats the principle I have quoted earlier, of recognizing and recording objections, and he sums up his method in regard to his main theory: 'I have for some time determined to give the arguments on *both* sides (as far as I could) instead of arguing on the mutability side alone.' [74]

Yet in spite of all the strain and effort of argument, he liked it and believed in it. In the concluding chapter of the 'Origin' he says: 'This whole volume is one long argument.' [75] It certainly is. Elsewhere he says of a personal conversation: 'I was particularly glad of our discussion after dinner; fighting a battle with you always clears my mind wonderfully.' [76] To get the mind clear, to illuminate and elucidate the complicated tangles of thought and theory, that was always the object, and if verbal battles helped it on, they were welcome.

But if he liked sincere, earnest argument, he detested controversy, the bitter war of excited personal feelings bent rather on achieving an individual triumph than on proving an abstract theory. He condemned and deplored the injury to science inevitably wrought by such disputes and had nothing but disgust for the manifestations of temper that were bound to accompany them: 'I went the other evening to the Zoölogical Society, where the speakers were snarling at each other in a manner anything but like that of gentlemen.' [77]

When his own views were involved in bitterness, as, alas, they too often were, he expressed the keenest regret: 'I often think that my friends . . . have good cause to hate me, for having stirred up so much mud, and led them into so much odious trouble. If I had been a friend of myself, I should have hated me.' [78] He early made up his mind to keep out of quarrels if possible, and he congratulated himself on the whole on his success: 'I rejoice that I have avoided controversies, and this I owe to Lyell, who many years ago, in reference to my geological works, strongly advised me never to get entangled in a controversy, as it rarely did any good and caused a miserable loss of time and temper.' [79]

Thus, whenever it was possible, he shunned dispute, and if, by any chance, haste and eagerness involved him in a mistaken cause, he bitterly regretted his blunder and was ready to acknowledge it with the utmost frankness. One of the most striking cases of this is that of the parallel roads of Glen Roy, as to which Darwin had developed a geological theory which he asserted with a good deal of conviction. A careful consideration of his opponent's arguments, obliged him to recognize that he was completely in the wrong, and he gave up, though with a pang: 'I am very poorly to-day, and very stupid, and hate everybody and everything. One lives only to make blunders.' [80] His acknowledgment of his error was ample and complete.

It was his natural frankness in admitting his mistakes and endeavoring to rectify them which made Darwin so attractive and engaging. Goethe complains of the disposition of many people to reiterate a misstatement because they have once made it. [81] Such reiteration did not appeal to Darwin in the least. Sometimes he was irritated and annoyed by the attitude of his adversaries, and he expressed the annoyance with the same outspokenness that he gave to other things; but there was never any attempt to conceal his blunders or to maintain his own positions simply because they were his.

Indeed, in this regard, as in all others, what distinguished him was a singular and charming candor. It is this which makes his letters so attractive and so revealing. They are not great literary letters. They are always written in haphazard fashion and with the utmost casual directness. But few correspondences of literary men or of any others reveal the man with such clear and winning amplitude. He opens his heart and leads you right into it without the least pretence of self-revelation, but simply as if he were thinking aloud to you, as he is. Take, for instance, among a bewildering mass of illustrations, his confession of the sense of inferiority in regard to Spencer: 'I feel rather mean when I read him: I could bear, rather enjoy feeling that he was twice as ingenious and clever as myself, but when I feel that he is about a dozen times my superior, even in the master art of wriggling, I feel aggrieved.' [82] Or this other acknowledgment to Hooker: 'How candidly and meekly you took my Jeremiad on your severity to second-class men. After I had sent it off, an ugly little voice asked me, once or twice, how much of my noble defence of the poor in spirit and in fact, was owing to your having not seldom smashed favorite notions of my own. I silenced the ugly little voice with contempt, but it would whisper again and again.' [83] The sense, the atmosphere, of a pervading candor, was what Huxley expressed so excellently when he spoke of Darwin's having 'a certain intense and almost passionate honesty by which all his thoughts and actions were irradiated, as by a central fire. It was this greatest and rarest of endowments which kept his vivid imagination and great speculative powers within due bounds . . . which made him accept criticisms and suggestions from anybody and everybody, not only without impatience, but with expressions of gratitude sometimes almost comically in excess of their value.' [84]

For the honesty and the candor not only led him to admit his own mistakes, but made him singularly ready to recognize the merits of others, and to tolerate not only their views but even their dogmatic assertion of them. He made mistakes all the time, and yet he knew that he was sincere and lofty in purpose. Why should not others be the same?

Why should not their theories be right and his wrong? 'It matters very little to any one except myself, whether I am a little more or less wrong on this or that point; in fact, I am sure to be proved wrong on many points.'[85] Of one who did not agree with him he could say: 'I know nothing of him excepting from his letters: these show remarkable talent, astonishing perseverance, much modesty, and what I admire, determined difference from me on many points.'[86] And how winning is his defense of blunderers, of those who do poor work which is not all poor: 'Shall you think me very impudent if I tell you that I have sometimes thought that . . . you are a little too hard on bad observers; that a remark made by a bad observer *cannot* be right; an observer who deserves to be damned you would utterly damn. I feel entire deference to any remark you make out of your own head; but when in opposition to some poor devil, I somehow involuntarily feel not quite so much.'[87]

The truth is, that Darwin's tolerance was based, as all real tolerance is apt to be, on the vast and haunting sense of his own ignorance. Again and again he repeats and emphasizes how little he knows, how little any one knows, and how petty, imperfect, and inadequate are the efforts of any and all of us to penetrate the veil of shrouding mystery which involves the deepest secrets of life. To probe this mystery the vague and flickering torch of reason is all that is given to us. And those who are most conversant with reason and make most use of it mistrust it most. When the far surer guidance of instinct fails us, reason is our only support, and we must employ it not only for the larger speculative purposes, but for the practical decisions. At its best, it is a bright and splendid instrument, incredibly keen and penetrating, and able to accomplish miracles in the hands of those who manipulate it skillfully. But it is an instrument as delicate as it is bright, and it loses point and edge, unless constant pains are taken to keep it in working condition. Also, it cuts both ways, and every way, and to even the expert manipulator, perhaps to him most of all, it is apt to be difficult, dangerous, treacherous.

There is the subtle, unfathomable connection of reason with our wishes, desires, and prejudices. A clever Frenchman said that reason was given us to enable us to justify the gratification of our passions, and when we see how the devices of logic may be used to work from any premises to any conclusion, one feels the force of the Frenchman's view.

DARWIN

No one was more aware than Darwin of these dangers and difficulties of reason, or of the endless possibilities of deception when one gives oneself up to that enchanting and deluding siren. He often emphasizes his distress and almost despair at finding himself making deductions quite different from those which others draw from the same facts. 'It is really disgusting and humiliating to see directly opposite conclusions drawn from the same facts.' [88] And again: 'Nothing is so vexatious to me, as so constantly finding myself drawing different conclusions from better judges than myself, from the same facts.' [89] And yet again: 'I hate beyond all things finding myself in disagreement with any capable judge, when the premises are the same.' [90]

These comments make us see clearly what Darwin's relation to reason was. Few thinkers have been so ready, so fertile, so abundant, so ingenious, yet at the same time so sober, so restrained and controlled.

With this analysis of his observation and his thought we are ready to take up the supreme interest of Darwin's life, the dramatic study of the conception, elaboration, promulgation, and triumph of his evolutionary theory.

CHAPTER III
DARWIN: THE DISCOVERER
I

THE word 'evolution' is so popularly accepted and so generally employed in connection with Darwin's theories that it will never be displaced; but it is not wholly satisfactory, because it always suggests progress from a lower to a higher and hence involves a difficult and invidious definition of terms. Some such phrase as 'descent with modification' would probably be more exact. But whatever the term used, to associate it as a scientific theory or discovery exclusively with Darwin or any other one man would be absurd. The natural hypothesis of earlier thinkers was that divine creative power, in whatever shape, had established the different forms of life on the earth pretty much as they exist to-day. But those who looked more deeply, were inclined to surmise, in view of the close and evident bonds of kinship between all living things, that variety had developed from comparative unity and that the vital impulse, having first appeared in elementary forms, became gradually elaborated into more and more complicated organisms. The

vast pains that Darwin took to substantiate this
view, together with his particular explanation of
how the process came about, have forever bound up
the idea of evolution with his name, but he did not
originate it nor did he claim to have done so.

The various hints and manifestations of earlier
evolutionary theory are admirably elucidated in
Professor Osborn's 'From the Greeks to Darwin.'
The vast curiosity and reflection of Aristotle anticipated here, as everywhere, and some of his sentences have a striking evolutionary bearing: 'Variety in animal life may be produced by variety of
locality.' [1] 'Locality will differentiate habits also;
for instance, rugged highlands will not produce the
same results as the soft lowlands.' [2] And Empedocles suggests Darwin's views even more directly.
Under the régime of Biblical and Christian tradition evolutionary thought naturally made little
progress. But with the greater freedom of the
eighteenth century, notions of modification by descent again appeared. In England Darwin's grandfather, Erasmus, the botanical poet, speculated
curiously on the subject, and there were various
other intimations, notably in Chambers's 'Vestiges
of Creation,' while Darwin himself felt that he was
much influenced by the geological theories of Lyell.

THE DISCOVERER

In Germany Goethe became profoundly interested in the metamorphoses of life. Especially in France Buffon and St.-Hilaire led up to the 'Philosophie Zoologique' of Lamarck, which propounded the theory of modification in a very definite form, and suggested the mode in which the modification was accomplished. Lamarck's idea was that plants and animals, by an inborn, vital impulse, adapted themselves to their environment, and that these adaptations were transmitted by inheritance. Thus wading birds acquired webbed feet and the neck of the giraffe was elongated in its effort to obtain its food from the branches of the trees. The great stumbling-block of this theory has always been the difficulty of proving that acquired adaptations are inherited.*

What is of interest to us, however, is Darwin's attitude toward his more immediate predecessors, Buffon, Lamarck, Chambers, etc. This attitude has been a matter of much comment by Samuel Butler and others and it is not perfectly easy to understand. That Darwin in his earlier thinking as

* Investigators have of course worked constantly and persistently upon this point and I find Professor William McDougall quoted in a Boston *Herald* editorial of August 16, 1926, as saying: 'Species may change and undergo evolution through the efforts of the individual parents to adapt themselves to conditions.'

well as in his later was influenced by previous investigators is evident enough, for instance in touches like that in the 'Voyage of the Beagle': 'Nature by making habit omnipotent, and its effects hereditary, has fitted the Fuegian to the climate and productions of his miserable country.' [3] Also, his frequent comments show that he knew what had been written before him and had profited by it, and in the later editions of the 'Origin' he took some pains to acknowledge the obligation. Yet his tone in his letters is by no means respectful and of Lamarck especially, who had done the most, it is difficult for him to speak without a sneer. Thus, in 1844 he writes: 'Heaven forefend me from Lamarck nonsense of a "tendency to progression," "adaptations from the slow willing of animals," etc.! But the conclusions I am led to are not widely different from his; though the means of change are wholly so.' [4] Again, a little later: 'With respect to books on this subject, I do not know any systematical ones, except Lamarck's which is veritable rubbish.' [5] And later still, in 1859, he writes to Lyell: 'You often allude to Lamarck's work; I do not know what you think about it, but it appeared to me extremely poor; I got not a fact or idea from it.' [6]

Various explanations of Darwin's treatment of

Lamarck have been offered. One at least, that of a
disposition to run down a predecessor from jealousy, we may exclude as absolutely as is possible
with poor human nature. Everything we know of
Darwin in other connections justifies us in doing
this. Professor Osborn, after referring to 'the dis-
dainful allusions to him [Lamarck] by Charles
Darwin (the only writer of whom Darwin ever
spoke in this tone)'[7] observes that 'it is very evident from all Darwin's criticisms of Lamarck, that
he had never studied him carefully in the original.'[8]
But against this view we have to set Darwin's own
comment (italics mine): 'What I consider, after
two deliberate readings, as a wretched book, and one
from which (I well remember my surprise) I gained
nothing.'[9] It is true that Darwin, as in the quotation above as to 'adaptations from the slow willing
of animals,' apparently misinterpreted Lamarck's
view of the self-adaptation of the individual to
its environment into the absurd assumption that
animals and even plants deliberately willed their
own evolutionary progress; but on the other hand
Darwin all his life and especially in his later period
wavered toward Lamarck's adaptation theories.
It has been suggested that in Darwin's university
years French thought and French scientists were

distinctly in disfavor and that Darwin imbibed an enduring dislike of them.[10] Darwin himself hints that he may have been influenced by a prejudice in favor of his grandfather as Lamarck's predecessor. But it seems more probable that he disliked Lamarck because he regarded him as a theorist and speculator who did not found his argument on a sufficiently broad basis of fact, whereas Darwin toiled for years at observation and experiment before he gave his theory to the world at all. This explanation is indicated in Darwin's remark to Lyell: 'As for Lamarck, as you have such a man as Grove with you, you are triumphant; not that I can alter my opinion that to me it was an absolutely useless book. Perhaps this was owing to my always searching books for facts.'[11] In any case one cannot help wishing that Darwin had spoken of a man so prominent and so highly esteemed as Lamarck a little differently.

II

Darwin first began to be interested in the idea of modification by descent during his voyage on the Beagle and in the year 1837.[12] In his earlier years he had been satisfied with the conventionally orthodox theological and scientific conception of

228

A PAGE FROM A NOTEBOOK OF 1837

the creation of distinct species, and all his youthful work had been on the basis of this view. Such phrases as the note, written in 1834, in Valparaiso: 'It seems not a very improbable conjecture that the want of animals may be owing to none having been created since this country was raised from the sea,' [13] are obviously significant of the earlier attitude. But as he observed more widely and became more and more impressed with the infinite diversity of forms and the delicacy of shading with which they pass into each other, the conviction grew that the possibilities of development were unlimited, and that individual differences might pass into varieties and these again into species, making the origin of varied life far simpler and more unified than had ever been imagined. And such an evolutionary process seemed much more in accord with general natural laws than the abrupt appearance of fixed, highly organized forms in sudden sufficiency. As he says, 'the subject haunted me,' and from a very early period he began making notes and memoranda of all observations that might bear for — or against — the gradual modification of species.

The difficulty was to imagine just how the process of modification was brought about, and until he could get some light on this point, his enthusiasm for the general idea was chilled and baffled. As we have seen, Lamarck's view, that living beings directly adapted themselves to their surroundings and then transmitted these adaptations to their descendants, seemed at least inadequate, and Darwin felt that the theory must have some more solid basis, if it was to prevail at all. He set his mind to work for months and months, and he applied the intellectual method which he himself has so admirably defined in a letter to his young son: 'I have been speculating last night what makes a man a discoverer of undiscovered things; and a most perplexing problem it is. Many men who are very clever — much cleverer than the discoverers — never originate anything. As far as I can conjecture, the art consists in habitually searching for the causes and meaning of everything which occurs.' [14]

Searching for the cause and meaning of everything which occurred, he at last achieved the discovery he was looking for, and so knew what is assuredly one of the greatest of spiritual delights. Largely by watching and studying the results of deliberate human selection with plants and animals, he was led to his great principle of natural selection, that is, assuming the tendency in all living beings to vary individually, that in the intense struggle for existence those variations which are beneficial and help the organism to live and prosper will be preserved and transmitted. The causes of variation, whether spontaneous or to be found in environment, Darwin never pretended entirely to explain. Of the principle of natural selection, or as Spencer phrased it in a form which Darwin admitted to be in some respects more satisfactory, 'the survival of the fittest,' perhaps its discoverer has given no better statement than the sentences in the second volume of the great work on 'Plants and Animals under Domestication': 'To consider the subject under this point of view is enough to strike one dumb with amazement. But our amazement ought to be lessened when we reflect that beings almost infinite in number, during an almost infinite lapse of time, have often had their whole organization rendered in some degree plastic, and that each slight modification of structure which was in any way beneficial under excessively complex conditions of life has been preserved, whilst each which was in any way injurious has been rigorously destroyed. And the long-continued accumulation of beneficial variations will infallibly have led to structures as diversified, as beautifully adapted for various purposes, and as excellently coördinated, as we see in the animals around us. Hence I have spoken of selection as the paramount power, whether applied by man to the formation of domestic breeds, or by nature to the production of species.' [15]

It is not to be supposed that the first grasp of evolution through variation and natural selection could have carried with it the full foresight of the enormous changes, mental, moral, and spiritual, that such a theory was likely to produce. Still, a mind so keen and active as Darwin's was bound to catch some suggestion of those changes. For instance, the astonishing and deadly ease with which the old workings of Providential adaptation and design slipped under the new light into mere operations of mechanical law could not fail to foreshadow the philosophical and theological upheaval that was sure to follow. A spirit trained in the conventional atmosphere of the early English nineteenth century must necessarily have regarded such an upheaval with a certain amount of question, awe, and even dismay; and Darwin indisputably had something of these feelings mingled with the triumphant joy of discovery.

It is profoundly characteristic of the man that he did not hasten to fling the discovery to the world, to get the immediate excitement and glory, leaving discussion and substantiation to come afterwards. He was so hesitant, so doubtful of his own methods and his own powers, that he delayed even to commit his conjectures to writing in his note-books, lest they should become hardened and distorted by the prejudice of statement and so misleading. His one idea was to get confirmation, by every line of study and experiment, and for twenty years he toiled with deliberate patience before he was willing to make the attempt to put his results into publishable shape.

And all the time there was the chance, perfectly present to his mind, that death might prevent him from ever making the discovery known. And all the time there was the chance that in the world of scientific thought that was seething about him some one else might anticipate him and propagate the idea, perhaps in a form less convincing and less substantial than he would be able to give it. Just as he was getting to the stage of preparation which he had aimed at, exactly this thing seemed likely to happen. In June 1858, Alfred Russel Wallace, a scientist of standing and ability, with whom Darwin had corresponded, sent him a paper largely anticipating Darwin's ideas on natural selection, so largely that Darwin wrote of it to Lyell: 'I never saw a more striking coincidence; if Wallace had my MS. sketch written out in 1842, he could not have made a better short abstract; . . . so all my originality, whatever it may amount to, will be smashed.' [16] And he even doubted whether he should make his views public at all, for fear of depriving Wallace of credit: 'I would far rather burn my whole book, than that he or any other man should think that I had behaved in a paltry spirit.' [17] The difficulty was adjusted, however, by friends, and a joint paper by Darwin and Wallace both, was read at the meeting of the Linnæan Society on July 1, 1858, giving the world the first inkling of what natural selection was to mean. Sir Joseph Hooker wrote prophetically of this meeting: 'The interest excited was intense, but the subject was too novel and too ominous for the old school to enter the lists, before armoring. After the meeting it was talked over with bated breath.' [18]

The relation between Darwin and Wallace in regard to priority of discovery is one of the finest things in the whole history of science. There was no jealousy, no bitterness, no acrimony, but instead a full recognition of each others' achievements, and a sympathetic understanding which ripened into a helpful and unbroken friendship. Wallace's statement of the matter long after Darwin's death, is as noble in its unselfishness as words can make it: 'But what is often forgotten by the press and the public is that the idea occurred to Darwin in 1838 . . . nearly twenty years earlier than to myself, and that during the whole twenty years he had been laboring collecting evidence from the vast mass of literature of biology, of horticulture, and of agriculture. . . . Such being the facts of the case, I should have had no cause for complaint if the respective shares of Darwin and myself . . . had been henceforth estimated as being roughly proportioned to the time we had each bestowed upon it . . . that is to say, as twenty years to one week.' [19] Darwin's summary, more general, is equally worthy of both: 'I hope it is a satisfaction to you to reflect — and very few things in my life have been more satisfactory to me — that we have never felt any jealousy towards each other, though in one sense rivals. I believe that I can say this of myself with truth, and I am absolutely sure that it is true of you.' [20]

The first promulgation of the Darwinian ideas, with those of Wallace, was therefore made in July, 1858. In the following year, November, 1859, 'The

Origin of Species' was published. Darwin himself regarded this book as a mere preliminary sketch, requiring to be supported and buttressed by confirmatory evidence of all sorts. But it at once overwhelmed the world, and has always been looked upon since as the cardinal statement of the theory. As Huxley said of it, 'It is doubtful if any single book, except the "Principia," ever worked so great and so rapid a revolution in science, or made so deep an impression on the general mind.'[21] And innumerable quotations could be drawn from other sources to the same effect.

III

The study of the complication of motives that prompts a man like Darwin, and many others, to reveal and establish a great scientific discovery in spite of violent opposition is profoundly curious and profitable. It seems to me that a main element in these motives, with the scientist, as with the artist and the politician and the actor and the preacher and the athlete alike, is ambition. As Darwin himself expresses it: 'The action of unconscious selection, as far as pigeons are concerned, depends on a universal principle in human nature, namely on our rivalry, and desire to outdo our neighbors. We see this in every fleeting fashion, even in our dress.'[22] And again: 'Man is the rival of other men; he delights in competition, and this leads to ambition which passes too easily into selfishness.'[23] The concrete essence of ambition is the desire for fame, to have one's efforts, one's powers, one's achievement, one's ego, recognized, appraised, established by the applause and commendation of one's fellow-men. And surely this desire in itself is a natural and even a laudable one, leading, as it does, to most useful and enduring accomplishment. The drawback is that the thirst for glory is so enticing, so overmastering, that it seduces men into strange and dubious methods of obtaining it. Glory, or notoriety, is got so often by base means, the trickster and the charlatan can so often snatch its rewards and laurels from honest labor and even from genius divinely endowed, that sincere and earnest spirits are impelled to disclaim the pursuit altogether, and to insist, perhaps with genuine self-deception, that fame as a motive hardly enters into their struggle at all. This contention is maintained the more easily, since it is evident that other motives, and those most powerful, do enter in. There is the restless, ever active disposition of human nature to be doing something, almost no matter what. To work, to create, to achieve, is to live. Nothing else can properly be called life. To have done great things, to be doing them, makes you feel that you exist, and why should you vex yourself with what other men think of them? Then for the scientist there is the sheer delight of adding one grain of truth to the slow accumulation of the centuries, as for the artist there is the splendid sense of having created something beautiful. You know it, you feel it: what do the others matter? And there is further the rich reward of believing, or hoping, that you are doing even a little to help or to enlighten your fellow-men, whether they are ever aware of it or not. Few things are more soothing or cheering to the soul than that. So that there have been thinkers and there have been artists who have said, and perhaps sincerely thought: 'I care not if some other man gets the credit of my work altogether. So the work is done, and I have done it, and know that I have done it, and it endures, and is worthy to endure, what does the name or the glory of it matter?' There are many who have said this, there may be some who have meant it; but surely there are few who have tried to do great things, and have not longed for the human recognition of them; and why should they not?

THE DISCOVERER

It is peculiarly interesting to trace the play of these motives in Darwin, because here, as everywhere, he has such an extraordinary, intimate frankness of revelation. The love of fame was strong in him, and he knew it. He tells us of his childhood: 'Some other recollections are those of vanity — namely, thinking that people were admiring me, in one instance for perseverance and another for boldness in climbing a low tree, and what is odder, a consciousness, as if instinctive, that I was vain, and contempt of myself.' [24] Of his earlier scientific years he writes: 'I was also ambitious to take a fair place among scientific men . . . whether more ambitious or less so than most of my fellow-workers, I can form no opinion.' [25] At a much later period he still recognizes the same stimulus: 'Without you have a very much greater soul than I have (and I believe that you have), you will find the medal a pleasant little stimulus; when work goes badly, and one ruminates that all is vanity, it is pleasant to have some tangible proof, that others have thought something of one's labors.' [26] And how charming is the frank admission that he hates to have glory snatched away from him: 'I always thought it very possible that I might be forestalled, but I fancied that I had a grand enough soul not to

lize general ideas that were vaguely present to many and needed only a vigorous expositor to give them universal acceptance. Doubtless there is a measure of truth in this view. Yet it must not be forgotten how much Darwin's character, his tact and reasonableness, his persistent energetic logic, above all the enormous industry and fidelity of his research entered into his final triumph. His own comment on this matter of the timeliness of his theories is exceedingly interesting: 'It has sometimes been said that the success of the "Origin" proved "that the subject was in the air," or "that men's minds were prepared for it." I do not think that this is strictly true, for I occasionally sounded not a few naturalists, and never happened to come across a single one who seemed to doubt about the permanence of species. . . . I tried once or twice to explain to able men what I meant by Natural Selection, but signally failed. What I believe was strictly true is that innumerable well-observed facts were stored in the minds of naturalists ready to take their proper places as soon as any theory which would receive them was sufficiently explained.' [31]

In any case, the evolutionary theory, when first propagated, was bitterly attacked, both by scientists and by others. Darwin's personal friends, and some of the younger men, who were less hardened in conservatism, supported him, though with more or less hesitation and reserve. But scientists of the older school, trained in established traditions, were generally most unfavorable. Some of them brought up the innumerable difficulties of which Darwin himself was only too well aware. Others resorted to the usual weapons of abuse and sarcasm. Owen in England and Agassiz in America represented perhaps the strongest conservative views. To them the Darwinian system was merely a passing heresy, which could not stand for a moment against the array of facts and arguments which they could bring from their vast experience and observation of the natural world.

The hostility of religious circles, aroused by the 'Origin' and increased by the later books, especially 'The Descent of Man,' was fiercer and less discriminating than that of the scientists. Perhaps the acme of it was reached in the savage interchange in which the Bishop of Oxford asked Huxley whether he 'was related by his grandfather's or grandmother's side to an ape' and Huxley retorted that a man had no reason to be ashamed of having an ape for a grandfather, but if he were to feel shame, it would be for an ancestor 'who not content with an equivocal success in his own sphere of activity, plunges into scientific questions with which he has no real acquaintance, only to obscure them by an aimless rhetoric, and distract the attention of his hearers from the real point at issue by eloquent digressions, and skilled appeals to religious prejudice.' [32]

This sort of thing was by no means agreeable to Darwin, and he repeatedly refers to the pain and distress it caused him. For example: 'I have just read the "Edinburgh," which without doubt is by ————. It is extremely malignant, clever, and I fear will be very damaging. He is atrociously severe on Huxley's lecture, and very bitter against Hooker. So we three *enjoyed* it together. Not that I really enjoyed it, for it made me uncomfortable for one night; but I have got quite over it to-day. It requires much study to appreciate all the bitter spite of many of the remarks against me; indeed I did not discover all myself. . . . It is painful to be hated in the intense degree with which ———— hates me.' [33]

What interests us is the attitude of Darwin in all the aspects of the struggle, and we find everywhere manifested and illustrated the mental and spiritual qualities which we have analyzed generally in the preceding chapters. Long and cruel as the controversy was, that large, tranquil disposition could not be warped or embittered, or substantially shaken in its kindly serenity.

And first there is the candor, the readiness to admit mistakes and errors, and to recognize the force and significance of an opponent's view and arguments. Darwin himself complains humorously of a weakness in this regard: 'My God, is not the case difficult enough, without its being, as I must think, falsely made more difficult? I believe it is my own fault —, my d——d candor.' [34] But, damned or not, it is a quality worth admiration. As Professor Osborn excellently puts it: 'If he were living, . . . he would be in the front line of inquiry, armed with matchless assemblage of fact, with experiment verification, and not least with incomparable candor and good-will. This bequest of a noble method is hardly less precious than the immortal content of "The Origin of Species" itself.' [35]

This is the language of an admirer. But it is curious to see how with critics and opponents

'To some kind of men
Their graces serve them but as enemies.'

Thus, even Alexander Agassiz, who was much more

favorably disposed to evolution and to Darwin than was his father, remarks on this point of candor: 'I was somewhat surprised in Darwin's Life to see the element of wishing his cause to succeed as a cause brought out so prominently. The one thing always claimed by Darwin's friends had been his absolute impartiality to his own case. Certainly his correspondence with Hooker, Huxley, and Gray shows no such thing.' [36] And others, distinctly more hostile, are much more severe, declaring that Darwin's passionate eagerness to prove his point was quite incompatible with any real fairness or breadth. But surely there is misunderstanding here. Any one can be impartial who is perfectly indifferent, and when you care not which side triumphs, there is no merit in seeing the justice of both. The charm and the interest of Darwin are precisely that he was devoted to his own theory, that it was the effort of his life to prove it, and yet that at the same time he could and did look for all the facts against it and even go to excess in allowing weight to the objections that could be opposed to him.

And as the candor was all the more notable because of the enthusiasm, so it was notable because it did not spring from a cold temperament, or an incapacity for natural human anger and indignation. Darwin enlarges, perhaps unduly, on his heat of temper in youth; and in age, though his control and his patience got the better of this, still the sparks would fly when unjust and unreasonable attack annoyed and irritated him. Thus, he cries out in regard to Owen: 'You would laugh if you could see how indignant all Owen's mean conduct about *E. Columbi* made me. I did not get to sleep till past 3 o'clock.' [37] And again, 'If Owen wrote the article "Oken" and the French work on the Archetype . . . , he never did a baser act. . . . You are so good a Christian that you will hardly understand how I chuckle over this bit of baseness.' [38] When an adversary, not content with rational argument, resorted to personal attack: 'I care not for his dull, unvarying abuse of me, and singular misrepresentation. But at p. 244 he in fact doubts my deliberate word, and that is the act of a man who has not the soul of a gentleman in him.' [39]

But, however at moments indignation might get the better of him, Darwin, as we have already seen, rarely allowed himself to be drawn into anything approaching controversy. Intelligent argument with those who had reasonable objections might be profitable, but where was the use of contending with those whose object was not to convince but to prevail? 'I do so hate controversy,' he cries, 'and feel I shall do it so badly.' [40] And elsewhere he writes, more generally: 'All that I think is that you will excite anger, and that anger so completely blinds every one, that your arguments would have no chance of influencing those who are already opposed to our views.' [41]

With this general attitude, it is interesting to find Darwin, in one of his few temptations to sharp retort, checked and repressed by the great fighter Huxley. Darwin submits the draft of a crisp letter, asking Huxley to criticize, and the latter suggests omissions: 'Though Thomson deserved it and more, I thought it would be better to refrain. If I say a savage thing, it is only "Pretty Fanny's way"; but if you do, it is not likely to be forgotten.' [42] Huxley and other friends also restrained Darwin in perhaps the most annoying of his controversial affairs, that with Samuel Butler over the translation of Krause's Life of Erasmus Darwin. It is not necessary for us to attempt to unthread the complicated tangle of this dispute, since we may start with the confident assumption that both men were perfectly sincere in their good intentions. The curious may read the whole story in the Life of Butler by Henry

Festing Jones, and it is pleasant to find that the biographers of Butler and of Darwin were able to come together and by comparing unprinted documents straighten out the difficulty to their mutual satisfaction.

With his fellow-workers, those who were following the same lines of research from the same general point of view, Darwin's relations were most cordial and sympathetic. There was no jealousy, no rivalry, no undue sensitiveness. We have indeed seen that in his treatment of his predecessors, notably Lamarck, there was a suggestion of what in any one else might be taken for a jealous attitude. But all the dealings with Wallace nobly refute the possibility of any such suggestion. And at all times and under all circumstances Darwin was ready to recognize and to proclaim the merits and achievements of those who were laboring beside him. When there was any question of priority in an idea or a discovery, he refused to assert himself unduly: 'I have always had a strong feeling that no one had better defend his own priority. I cannot say that I am as indifferent to the subject as I ought to be, but one can avoid doing anything in consequence.' [43] When a scientist, whether known or unknown, applied to him for assistance or suggestion, he was always ready to supply it, so far as was in his power. Above all, he was appreciative, almost to excess, of any assistance that was rendered to him, and his gratitude to his friends for supporting and sustaining him and forwarding his views is touching in its naïve earnestness. To Huxley, to Hooker, to Lyell, to Gray, to Häckel, to a dozen others, he speaks with enthusiastic acknowledgment of their efforts and their contributions, and, as Huxley points out, he was ready to bestow almost the same gratitude for services that in themselves appeared to be absurdly insignificant.

For he had a singular humility, most notable and appealing in a man of such distinguished power and achievement. 'A mind conspicuous for its powerful humility and strong gentleness,' is Huxley's vivid characterization.[44] Again and again he expresses distrust of his powers, sense of inadequacy and incompetence, keen consciousness of limitation. Such phrases as the following from the book on Orchids, are constantly recurring: 'To any one with more knowledge than I possess, it would be an interesting subject to trace the gradations between the several species and groups of species in this great and closely-connected order.'[45] Sometimes the expression of humility is direct. 'Any one with ordinary faculties, if he had *patience* enough and plenty of time could have written my book.'[46] Sometimes there is a humorous assertion of the contrary which is quite as significant: 'I should rather think there was a good chance of my becoming the most egotistical man in Europe. What a proud preëminence!'[47] Occasionally the profession of humility is so extreme, as in the sentence in regard to Owen, 'The Londoners say he is mad with envy because my book has been talked about; what a strange man to be envious of a naturalist like myself, immeasurably his inferior!'[48] that critics disposed to find fault have discerned something of affectation in it. It is of the nature of the deepest humility always to expose itself to such accusations as this; but surely no one can study Darwin carefully, can be familiar with his work in all its aspects, and not set him down as one of the most sincerely humble spirits that ever lived.

V

This humility and feeling of his own incompetence made Darwin keenly alive to the difficulties connected with his great undertaking and gave him such a clear sense of them that at times he felt incapable of solving them at all. As he says in the sixth chapter of the 'Origin': 'Long before the reader has arrived at this part of my work, a crowd of difficulties will have occurred to him. Some of them are so serious that to this day I can hardly reflect on them without being in some degree staggered.' [49]

Take one of the most striking, if not the most crucial difficulties, one which puzzled and perplexed Darwin from the first and was made a fruitful text for criticism by his adversaries, the development of the eye. Was it to be supposed that so delicate, so complex, and so highly adapted an organ could be produced by mere accidental variation working through inheritance and the gradual survival of the fittest? And Darwin investigated and compared and reflected, until he was ready to state his position thus: 'Reason tells me, that if numerous gradations from a simple and imperfect eye to one complex and perfect can be shown to exist, each grade being useful to its possessor, as is certainly the case; if further the eye ever varies and the variations be inherited, as is likewise certainly the case; and if such variations should be useful to any animal under changing conditions of life, then the difficulty of believing that a perfect and complex eye could be formed by natural selection, though insuperable by our imagination, should not be considered subversive of the theory.' [50]

Sometimes the difficulties appear in themselves insignificant, yet their bearing is such as to make them of extreme importance. For example, how the useful institution of neuter insects could be developed by inheritance was a terrible problem. It 'at first appeared to me insuperable, and actually fatal to the whole theory.' [51] Study and observation wear it away; yet it is disposed of with the candid remark: 'I must confess, that, with all my faith in natural selection, I should never have anticipated that this principle could have been efficient in so high a degree, had not the case of these neuter insects led me to this conclusion.' [52] Or there is the coloring of the peacock's tail, which has to be explained by extreme wrestlings of logical ingenuity. And again, as compared with these seemingly petty obstacles, there are the great questions involved in the essential tissue of the theory itself. There are the gaps, the breaks, the missing links, not only between man and his simian ancestors, but completing all the gradations between all the existing forms of development. Many and many an hour, and one may say, many a year of anxious thought did Darwin bestow on this point. He could meet it only with such eager comment as he makes after his prolonged study of the orchids: 'In the comparatively few orchids described in this volume, so many and such plainly-marked gradations in the structure of the rostellum have been described, . . . that we may well believe, if we could see every orchid which has ever existed throughout the world, we should find all the gaps in the existing chain, and every gap in many lost chains, filled up by a series of easy transitions.'[53] And there were such vast problems as sexual selection and pangenesis, which we discussed in a previous chapter, and there was even the central element of natural selection itself, which in darker moments seemed but a weak agency for sustaining the whole world: 'If I think continuously on some half-dozen structures of which we can at present see no use, I can persuade myself that natural selection is of quite subordinate importance.'[54]

The interesting aspect of this matter of difficulty, as with other things, is Darwin's way of meeting and facing it. There was an excitement, a stimulus, undoubtedly, a joy in attacking tough problems and conquering them. But there was also a pervading consciousness of what the difficulties were, and some have even thought an almost too pervading disposition to go out of one's way to deal with them. As Huxley puts it: One 'who desires to attack Mr. Darwin has only to read his works with a desire to observe not their merits but their defects, and he will find ready to hand more adverse suggestions than are likely ever to have suggested themselves to his own sharpness, without Mr. Darwin's self-denying aid.'[55]

And there is always the appreciation, in handling the difficulties, of the danger in over-ingenuity, of the subtle possibilities of betrayal by reason ever toiling with intense ardor to arrive at its preconceived ends. 'God knows I have never shirked a difficulty,' said Darwin.[56] But the danger lies not only in shirking, but in the dissolving, transforming power of prejudice and enthusiasm. Here again Darwin tried to be ever on his guard: 'I am fairly rabid on the question, and therefore, if not wrong already, am pretty sure to become so.'[57] He would not be misled, or fooled, or betrayed: 'As I read on, I felt not a little dumbfounded, and thought to myself that whenever I came to this subject I should have to be savage against myself.'[58]

But you can never be sure that you have been

savage enough, and there are moments when un-
expected obstacles make you mistrust your theory,
mistrust your method, mistrust your reasoning
power. 'If it could be proved that any part of the
structure of any one species had been formed for the
exclusive good of another species, it would annihi-
late my theory.' [59]   And who knows that it cannot be
proved? After months of study, a clear statement
of opposing facts seems for the moment to demolish
everything. 'You give all the facts so clearly and
fully, that it is impossible to help speculating on the
subject; but it drives me to despair, for I cannot
gulp down your continent; and not to be able to do
so gives, in my eyes, the multiple creationists an
awful triumph.' [60]   And with his extraordinary gift
of direct self-revelation, Darwin sums up the state
of mind in one vivid sentence: 'Your letter actually
turned me sick with panic.' [61]

Thus there are times of discouragement and disgust. One gets to feel that one has utterly overestimated one's work and one's powers. One con-
cocts 'pleasant little stinging remarks for reviews,
such as "Mr. Darwin's head seems to have been
turned by a certain degree of success, and he thinks
that the most trifling observations are worth
publication."' [62]   One concludes that all the years

of vast labor have been given to no valid result and that one had better have cultivated one's cabbages with health and quietness: 'At present I feel sick of everything, and if I could occupy my time and forget my daily discomforts, or rather miseries, I would never publish another word.'[63] Such periods of depression in Darwin are peculiarly interesting, because he was by no means of a melancholy temperament, nor, in spite of his nervous weakness, was he inclined to a fretful or morbid pessimism. Yet, even with all his courage and all his patience, with all his past labor and all his victory, there were moments toward the end when the grave seemed inviting for its mere vastness of repose, without any definite prospect of anything further: 'I am rather despondent about myself, and my troubles are of an exactly opposite nature to yours, for idleness is downright misery to me, as I find here, as I cannot forget my discomfort for an hour. I have not the heart or strength at my age to begin any investigation lasting years, which is the only thing which I enjoy; and I have no little jobs which I can do. So I must look forward to Down graveyard as the sweetest place on earth.'[64]

VI

The recognition and the accumulation of difficulties naturally involved modification of views. Indeed any really vital theory is bound to develop and modify itself with the vitality of the man who holds it. And Darwin was as vital as any man, and his theories as vital as any ever were. No man ever recognized more fully than he the desirability, the necessity of modification: 'I look at it as absolutely certain that very much in the *Origin* will be proved rubbish; but I expect and hope that the framework will stand.'[65] He groans over the burden and difficulty of perpetual correcting: 'I am grieved to hear that you think I must work in the notes in the text; but you are so much better a judge that I will obey.'[66] Again: 'It is only about two years since last edition of *Origin*, and I am disgusted to find how much I have to modify, and how much I ought to add.'[67] Nevertheless, as the successive editions of the 'Origin' and the other books show, he continued to add and to alter and to correct, to the very end. The minute, thoughtful, and far-reaching character of these alterations shows well in the concluding sentence of the eleventh chapter of the 'Origin,' which in the first edition read, 'old forms having been supplanted by new and improved forms of life produced by the laws of variation still acting round us and preserved by natural selection,' and later, 'old forms having been supplanted by new and improved forms of life, the products of Variation and the Survival of the Fittest.'

Besides revision in detail, there was of course always a tendency to larger modifications of the general theory. Ingenious and far-reaching as natural selection was, the difficulties connected with it were so immense, that the loyalty of even its discoverer at times necessarily wavered, or perhaps we should say better, his enthusiasm heated and cooled. Moreover, natural selection depended upon variation, and variation to Darwin was always an inexplicable puzzle, for which no solution or too many might be found. Disinclined as he was to accept or even to respect his predecessors, Buffon and Lamarck, Darwin in later years, when the pressure on natural selection became fiercer, seemed to turn more to the adaptive solutions of these predecessors. As Professor Morgan puts it: 'Despite the contempt with which Darwin referred to Lamarck's theory, he himself, as we have seen, often made use of the principle of the inheritance of acquired characters, and even employed the same illustrations cited by Lamarck.'[68] And Professor Osborn indicates admirably the gradual process of the change which took place in Darwin's attitude: 'Starting with some leaning towards the theories of modification of Buffon and Lamarck, he reached an almost exclusive belief in his own theory, and then gradually inclined to adopt Buffon's and then Lamarck's theories as well, until in his maturest writings he embraced a threefold causation in the origin of species.'[69] The drift towards Lamarck is well shown in a passage of a letter to Galton, written in 1875: 'If this implies that many parts are not modified by use and disuse during the life of the individual, I differ widely from you, as every year I come to attribute more and more to such agency.'[70] At the same time, to the very end natural selection remained in Darwin's mind not only the quintessence of his theorizing, but the prime agent by which modification had been accomplished. In 'The Descent of Man' he explains and in a manner excuses any earlier undue insistance upon it, but also reiterates his firm faith in its great, if not omnipotent efficacy: 'If I have erred in giving to natural selection great power, which I am very far from admitting, or in having exaggerated its power, which is in itself probable, I have at least, as I hope, done good service in

aiding to overthrow the dogma of separate creations.' [71]

VII

So through the sixties and seventies the battle for
evolution went merrily on, and before Darwin's
death in 1881 it was evident that the scientific
world was largely converted and still more evident
that the theory had taken solid hold upon the popular mind. Even in the sixties Charles Kingsley
could write to F. D. Maurice: 'The state of the
scientific mind is most curious; Darwin is conquering everywhere, and rushing in like a flood, by the
mere force of truth and fact.' [72] Darwin himself was
no aggressive fighter, though perhaps his quiet,
persistent, logical statement of facts went further
than fighting. But he had fighting followers, and
they pushed his cause with an energy and dogma-
tism which he himself could hardly have manifested. In England Spencer gave the theory the
metaphysical and philosophical sanction and support which Darwin was not equipped to render, and
the brilliant, ardent eloquence of Huxley paralyzed
opponents with incisive argument and stinging
ridicule. In America Asa Gray, the great botanist,
was a convert from the beginning and a most help-

ful disciple, and his aid was peculiarly welcome to Darwin, because Gray's eager orthodoxy was useful in conciliating many whose prejudices would naturally have been most adverse. Darwin repeatedly spoke of Gray as understanding his ideas better and expounding them more effectively than almost any one. John Fiske was also a valuable champion from the more philosophical side. In Germany Weisman and Häckel were the most prominent apostles, and immensely effective, though, with thorough-going Teutonic logic, they were ready to push conclusions to lengths that were not always acceptable to Darwin himself.

The amount of popular interest is probably best shown in the extensive sale of Darwin's books. 'The Origin of Species' was successful at once. It went through edition after edition, in Darwin's lifetime six in all, and was translated into numerous foreign languages. The later books, even those of a more technical character, sold like popular fiction, and the last one, on the apparently uninviting subject of earthworms, found many readers everywhere.

Darwin was of course quite conscious of his growing triumph. Even hostility, animosity, execration, painful as they might be, afforded evidence of

power and achievement. And he would not have
been human, had he not relished the varied testimony of respect and admiration which came to
him from every quarter. His natural distrust of
himself was so great that it was hard for him to
believe in success, even when it came, and before it
came, he deprecated any attempt to discount it:
'Please do not say to any one that I thought my
book on Species would be fairly popular, and have a
fairly remunerative sale (which was the height of
my ambition), for if it prove a dead failure, it
would make me the more ridiculous.'[73] Yet, however one might shrink and distrust oneself, to enter
a great scientific meeting and have every one present rise to do one honor was undeniably agreeable.
And, with his unfailing frankness, Darwin admits
that praise was pleasant, and one could not have
too much of it, provided one felt that it was in a
measure deserved: 'You pay me a superb compli-
ment, and as I have just said to my wife, I think
my friends must perceive that I like praise, they
give me such hearty doses.'[74] Also, with equal
frankness, he makes it plain in his autobiographical
sketch that he realizes how great the success was
and that it implied a certain prospect of permanence: 'My books have sold largely in England,

have been translated into many languages, and passed through several editions in foreign countries. I have heard it said that the success of a work abroad is the best test of its enduring value. I doubt whether this is at all trustworthy; but judged by this standard my name ought to last for a few years.' [75] When he died, he was unquestionably rated as one of the very first, if not the first, among the scientific men of his time.

And it is equally unquestionable that his reputation has rather increased than diminished ever since. '"Before and after Darwin" will always be the *ante et post urbem conditam* of biological history,' says Professor Osborn. [76] Naturally Darwin's theories have been criticized and attacked and largely modified by later investigations and discoveries. To Darwin himself variation, as the basis of natural selection, was the difficult, inexplicable point, and the experiments of Mendel, the mutation theory of De Vries, and many other lines of research have put the subject of variation in a new light. Natural Selection has been and will be the subject of controversy, both as to its working and as to the extent of its efficacy. Darwin's inimitable caution left the way open for all these investigations, as is so well indicated in the excellent sentence of Professor Whitehead: 'Darwin's own writings are for all time a model of refusal to go beyond the direct evidence and of careful retention of every possible hypothesis.'[77]

Yet, after fifty years of discussion and argument, Darwin's main positions hold their own with extraordinary tenacity. In the very latest word on the subject Professor Parker says: 'It is to the credit of Charles Darwin and his body of able supporters that the scientific world was finally brought to accept the principle of descent with modification and natural selection as the means whereby it was accomplished.'[78] Professor Conklin affirms that: 'The only scientific explanation of such adjustment or fitness is Darwin's principle of natural selection of the fit and elimination of the unfit, and it is eloquent testimony to the greatness of Darwin that more and more this great principle is being recognized as the only mechanistic explanation of adaptation.'[79] And Professor Osborn is equally emphatic: 'In my opinion natural selection is the only cause of evolution which has thus far been discovered and demonstrated.'[80] While from a more abstractly philosophical point of view the emphatic recently written words of Professor Ralph Barton Perry, give ample support to the general Darwinian position: 'In truth there is no gulf between man and the animal. We cannot deny to the latter sensibility, memory, and intelligence. The facts which prove it would fill volumes. . . . The animal has feelings of mother love, attachment, and devotion. It differs from us in degree only; its "soul" is to ours what the bud is to the flower and fruit.'[81]

But, independent of all agreement or disagreement with Darwin's theories, the striking thing is the consensus of scientists in praise of the man, and the recognition of his effort and method and life as a model for all scientific workers. It is rare that praise is so unalloyed, so persistent, and so complete. In this connection it is interesting to compare the nature of the glory of the poet, Shakespeare, for example, with that of the scientific writer. Shakespeare is not only remembered, he is read. Every successive generation takes up his plays for themselves, reads into them its own passions and experiences, and thus makes them a perennial possession of humanity, quite independent of their author. The works of Darwin, or of any other scientist, have no such enduring value for actual perusal. The curious study them for historical record. But for the mass of mankind and even of scientists, a large part of them has entered into universal knowledge and may be read in any textbook, and the remainder has become obsolete and of no value except for what it meant in an earlier day. The scientist's name becomes detached from the work, even though he remains great because he did it. Yet the name, in spite of being thus detached, perhaps all the more because it is detached, shines like a star through century after century.

CHAPTER IV
DARWIN: THE LOSER
I

At different times Darwin commented on the gradually increasing absorption of his life by scientific pursuits and on the consequent atrophy of other intellectual and spiritual interests, which in earlier days had meant a good deal to him. In other words he was illustrating the favorite text of Sainte-Beuve, 'All longings fail except that to understand.' Sometimes he expresses this loss with terse vigor: 'It is an accursed evil to a man to become so absorbed in any subject as I am in mine.'[1] Or again: 'It is a horrid bore to feel as I constantly do, that I am a withered leaf for every subject except Science. It sometimes makes me hate Science, though God knows I ought to be thankful for such a perennial interest, which makes me forget for some hours every day my accursed stomach.'[2] And elsewhere he analyzes it with more elaborate regretful curiosity: 'My mind seems to have become a kind of machine for grinding general laws out of large collections of facts, but why this should have

128

THE STUDY AT DOWN

caused the atrophy of that part of the brain alone, on which the higher tastes depend, I cannot conceive. A man with a mind more highly organized or better constituted than mine, would not, I suppose, have thus suffered; and if I had to live my life again, I would have made a rule to read some poetry or listen to some music at least once every week; for perhaps the parts of my brain now atrophied would thus have been kept active through use.'[3]

Having recently had occasion to make a somewhat extended study of Darwin's remarkable contemporary the evangelist D. L. Moody, I have been struck by this similarity of lack of general interest in both of them. Darwin was of course a far better educated man fundamentally than Moody. But in both, their very bigness and power made the one engrossing passion — about as different in the two cases as can be imagined — dwarf and drive out the varied distractions and desires which relieve and stimulate the curiosity or the indolence of more ordinary men. So far as Darwin is concerned, with the exaggeration natural to reminiscence, he perhaps somewhat overestimated both the original aptitude and the later atrophy. But it is exceedingly instructive to trace his relation to the various occupations and experiences of life outside of the scientific.

Take first the external human interests, other than purely social. In the larger movements of history Darwin seems not to have been particularly well versed or to have concerned himself very much with them. Of course, in relying upon his volumes of published letters as evidence, we must remember that those volumes were naturally edited with a view in the main to scientific pursuits, and therefore it is to be expected that other interests should figure less conspicuously. Still the testimony, both positive and negative, to the unimportance of those interests is very decided. As to this matter of history, Darwin himself tells us that he read the historians in his youth. He even insists that when he had lost æsthetic pleasures, 'books on history, biographies, and travels . . . and essays on all sorts of subjects interest me as much as ever they did.'[4] Of his earlier life he records that 'I used to sit for hours reading the historical plays of Shakespeare, generally in an old window in the thick walls of the school.'[5] Perhaps on this Shakespearean basis, he retains, with many other English conventions, that of reverence for rank, though no more natural democrat ever lived, and he makes gentle fun of himself for his snobbishness: 'I have the true English reverence for rank, and therefore liked to hear about the Princess Royal.'[6]

Nevertheless, in his letters and in his books, you get the sense that the great currents of development in Europe and in the world were not familiar to his thought. With the unfailing candor, he admits this: 'I believe your criticism is quite just about my deficient historic spirit, for I am aware of my ignorance in this line.'[7] And an acute and sympathetic analyst of his work, points out that it suffered to some extent from the deficiency. The tendency to extend evolutionary analogies from the individual to society was partly Darwin's fault, says this critic, because of his 'embarking upon the discussion of social and moral matters, in "The Descent of Man"; matters concerning which he was little better informed than any other non-specialist.'[8]

In contemporary politics it was not to be expected that Darwin should have much immediate concern. One can hardly imagine a man less likely to choose an active political career, or on the whole less adapted to it, though the tact which enabled him to deal successfully with his fellow-scientists would no doubt have been helpful in more prac-

tical spheres. There are occasional glimpses of his
taking some part in local interests, and for a time
at any rate he attended to the judicial duties which
we so generally associate with the English country
squire: 'I attended the Bench on Monday, and was
detained in adjudicating some troublesome cases
one and one half hours longer than usual, and came
home utterly knocked up, and cannot rally.'[9]

Darwin would not have been an Englishman, if
he had not entertained political opinions of some
sort. He could not pretend to escape the tradition
so strongly planted in the blood of the race. He
does indeed resent the suggestion that politics are
more important than science: 'Did you see a sneer
some time ago in the *Times* about how incompar-
ably more interesting politics were compared with
science even to scientific men? . . . Jeffrey, in one of
his letters, I remember, says that making an effective speech in Parliament is a far grander thing
than writing the grandest history. All this seems to
me a poor short-sighted view.'[10] But he has been
brought up a Whig, a Liberal, and Whig prejudices
are inherent in his system. This was true in the
early days of the Beagle voyage: 'The Captain does
everything in his power to assist me, and we get on
very well, but I thank my better fortune he has not

made me a renegade to Whig principles.'[11] And it remained true to old age. When answering a questionaire in 1873, he described himself as 'Liberal or Radical,'[12] but the radicalism was of a very conservative and English order.

The Whig partisanship even shows itself in quite normal fashion in hatred of the Tories, and on this head the tolerant and kindly scientist expresses himself with a rather amusing bitterness: 'Thank God, the cold-hearted Tories, who, as J. Mackintosh used to say, have no enthusiasm, except against enthusiasm, have for the present run their race.'[13] But these outbursts are not to be taken very seriously.

There are occasional glimpses of interest in current public men and current public affairs. Lord Bryce gives a striking account of a visit which Gladstone paid to the great thinker. Darwin's comment was, 'he seemed to be quite unaware that he was a great man, and talked to us as if he had been an ordinary person like ourselves.' On which Bryce remarks: 'The friend who was with me and I could not but look at each other and exchange covert smiles. We were feeling toward Darwin just as he had felt toward Gladstone.'[14] During the early portion of the Franco-German War Darwin's sympathy, like that of many Englishmen, was

133

with Germany: 'I have not yet met a soul in England who does not rejoice in the splendid triumph of Germany over France: it is a most just retribution against that vainglorious, war-liking nation.' [15] But the struggles of party politics, as they went on about him, aroused little attention and little ardor.

There was, however, one political event of his time that called forth Darwin's keen sympathy and extended comment, and that was the American Civil War. As is well known, English opinion was much divided on this question, and the prejudices of the upper class, at any rate among the more conservative, were in favor of the South. Although Darwin was by no means confident that the North would win, he was strongly on that side from the start, and his numerous letters to Asa Gray show how decided his feeling was.

The feeling was not based on the abstract political and constitutional considerations that appealed to Americans, but on Darwin's rooted, bitter antipathy to the system of slavery in any form. When he was in South America with the Beagle, he had plenty of opportunity to watch the working of human servitude, and it disgusted and repelled him beyond measure. 'To this day, if I hear a distant scream, it recalls with painful vividness my feelings, when passing a house near Pernambuco, I heard the most pitiable moans, and could not but suspect that some poor slave was being tortured, yet knew that I was as powerless as a child even to remonstrate. . . . Near Rio de Janeiro I lived opposite to an old lady, who kept screws to crush the fingers of her female slaves. I have stayed in a house where a young household mulatto, daily and hourly, was reviled, beaten, and persecuted enough to break the spirit of the lowest animal.'[16] As a result of these experiences and many others, Darwin imbibed a detestation of slavery and slave-holders which lasted through life, and which led him to oppose them where he could, whether in England or America.

The hostility to slavery was based even more deeply on an intense hatred of cruelty, barbarity, and the infliction of physical suffering of any sort. The dislike of such suffering was so keen that from the start it incapacitated Darwin for the medical profession, which his father would have been glad to see him follow. He could not bear the sight of blood, and fled from an operation with disgust. Ill-treatment of animals was especially tormenting to him, and he interfered to prevent it, when he could: 'He returned one day from his walk pale and faint having seen a horse ill-used, and from the agitation of violently remonstrating with the man.' [17]

With such a general sensibility, Darwin's attitude towards vivisection is extremely curious. Knowing as he did the importance of animal experiment, he could not possibly range himself on the side of the anti-vivisectionists. But he supported every effort to have humanity legally emphasized and rigidly insisted upon. The nature of his feeling in the matter appears clearly in a passage of 'The Descent of Man': 'Every one has heard of the dog suffering under vivisection, who licked the hand of the operator; this man, unless the operation was fully justified by an increase of our knowledge, or unless he had a heart of stone, must have felt remorse to the last hour of his life.' [18]

In sociological questions of a broader bearing, which made no such immediate appeal to his susceptibilities, Darwin took much less interest. Now and then some special point arouses him. He was excited about any attempt to interfere with the marriage of cousins, because he had married his cousin and had in consequence largely investigated the subject. [19] He was decidedly opposed to the English tradition of primogeniture, and felt its unfairness. On the land-question he writes to Wallace:

'I see you are going to write on the most difficult political question, the land. Something ought to be done; but what, is the rub.'[20] In the same spirit of remoteness and uncertainty, he writes also to Wallace in regard to Henry George's 'Progress and Poverty': 'I will certainly order "Progress and Poverty," for the subject is a most interesting one. But I read many years ago some books on political economy, and they produced a disastrous effect on my mind, viz., utterly to distrust my own judgment on the subject, and to doubt much every one else's judgment. So I feel sure that Mr. George's book will only make my mind worse confounded than it is at present.'[21] But it is clear that the remoteness did not imply contempt or cynical disregard, merely a feeling of complete inability and diffidence in regard to economic problems, and one is slow to condemn this state of mind, when one thinks that such problems are usually dealt with and solved, if it can be called so, by those in whose equipment freedom from diffidence is the most aggressive and impressive instrument.

II

With artistic and general æsthetic matters, Darwin, at any rate in later years, was even more indifferent than with political. It is true that his scientific investigations sometimes involved the abstract analysis of æsthetics: 'I agree with what you say about beauty. I formerly thought a good deal on the subject, and was led quite to repudiate the doctrine of beauty being created for beauty's sake.'[22] The theory of sexual selection, as presented in 'The Descent of Man,' necessitated a good deal of discussion of the susceptibility to color and form and to music. But such æsthetic discussion has nothing whatever to do with æsthetic enjoyment.

One thing may be said in regard to Darwin; with art as with everything else, he was absolutely free from pretense. He says of one writer, 'The pretentiousness of her style is extremely disagreeable, not to say nauseous to many persons.'[23] Anything artificial, anything affected, was peculiarly repugnant to him, and never under any circumstances would he have pretended to admire or to appreciate a work of art that really left him cold. Indeed it was partly his intense wish not to appear to feel what he did not feel that made him inclined to underestimate his artistic pleasure as compared with the raptures of those who exclaimed conventionally over what they neither understood nor enjoyed.

Nevertheless, it seems unquestionable that art in its varied forms hardly afforded Darwin the delight and solace that it brings to many persons. The theater he cared little for at any period of his life. The effort, fatigue, and constraint outweighed the charm. Mrs. Darwin, who was a lover of average plays, though she found Shakespeare tedious and said so with something of her husband's candor, is quite anxious on the subject: 'The real crook in my lot I have withheld from you, but I must own it to you sooner or later. It is that he has a great dislike of going to the play, so that I am afraid we shall have some domestic dissensions on that head.'[24] Later she takes him to see Macready in 'Richelieu' and hopes that he is getting converted, but there are no signs that the hopes were finally realized.

With the plastic arts the case is somewhat better. There is little reference to architecture. One passage in a letter seems to suggest the feeling of cathedral grandeur, but the æsthetic quickly turns into the scientific bearing: 'Possibly the sense of sublimity excited by a grand cathedral may have some connection with the vague feelings of terror and superstition in our savage ancestors, when they entered a great cavern or gloomy forest.'[25] As regards pictures, his son thinks that he did keep up his love of them to a certain extent.[26] His biographer remarks: 'His love of pictures as a young man is almost a proof that he must have had an appreciation of a portrait as a work of art, not as a likeness.'[27] And the biographer adds, with entire justice: 'This way of looking at himself as an ignoramus in all matters of art, was strengthened by the absence of pretence, which was part of his character.'[28] The immediate recognition of a Salvator Rosa scene in one of the Beagle experiences shows an acquaintance with painting in its different forms and periods.[29] Yet pictures make a different showing in Darwin's letters from what they have in Edward FitzGerald's, for instance.

The form of art which meant most to Darwin and into which he seemed to enter with the nearest approach to ecstasy was music. Here again, there is a good deal of theoretical discussion, which at times appears of a nature to dampen emotional enjoyment. But there can be no question that with Darwin as a young man the emotional enjoyment was there, and sincere, and profound, even at times overmastering. He does indeed confess that his musical ear was not fine or perfect: 'I am so utterly destitute of an ear, that I cannot perceive a discord, or keep time and hum a tune correctly; and it is a mystery how I could possibly have derived pleasure from music.'[30] But it is manifest that he did derive such pleasure, and went out of his way to seek it: 'I also got into a musical set. . . . From associating with these men, and hearing them play I acquired a strong taste for music, and used very often to time my walks so as to hear on week days the anthem in King's College Chapel.'[31]

The love was for good music, too, not by any means for what was trashy or cheap. He liked Beethoven and Händel, had the natural instinct for the high and fine, in this as in other matters. Mrs. Darwin took him to classical concerts and he responded much more heartily than to the theater. He liked to have his wife and his sisters play to him, and when he was absent with the Beagle, he wrote: 'I hope your musical tastes continue in due force. I shall be ravenous for the pianoforte.'[32]

And the enjoyment was not merely perfunctory, but went deep, and took hold of the nerves. 'At the end of one of the parts, which was exceedingly impressive, he turned round to me and said, with a deep sigh, "How's your backbone?" He often spoke of coldness or shivering in his back on hearing beautiful music.'[33] The references to this thrill, this tension of nervous musical excitement, occur occasionally even in Darwin's more scientific works.

And then there is the recurring doubt, the mistrust of one's sincerity, the desperate dread of sentimental convention in these artistic matters: 'This gave me intense pleasure, so that my backbone would sometimes shiver. I am sure that there was no affectation or mere imitation in this taste, for I used generally to go by myself to King's College, and I sometimes hired the chorister boys to sing in my rooms.' [34]

But, affectation or not, the musical enthusiasm vanished, and the encroaching, all-absorbing growth of the scientific preoccupation crowded it out. Indeed, any one who is susceptible to musical delight, appreciates how elusive it is, how much it depends upon favorable conditions and surroundings, and how peculiarly its delicate and subtle quality is subject to erasure by distractions of a different order. And Darwin's comment on the disappearance of his pleasure in music is: 'I have said that formerly pictures gave me considerable, and music very great delight. . . . I have also almost lost my taste for pictures or music. Music generally sets me thinking too energetically on what I have been at work on, instead of giving me pleasure.' [35]

With the enjoyment of beauty in literary forms, Darwin's sense of loss was quite as keen as with music. Of the higher and finer elements of style and imagination there is little evidence that he was conscious. Such consciousness would not seem very compatible with his remark about Buckle: 'To my taste he is the very best writer of the English language that ever lived, let the other be who he may.'[36]

In this connection it is interesting to consider Darwin's own style, as it appears in the vast mass of his production, running probably, letters and all, to over two million words. In this mass there are occasional passages of appealing beauty or startling effectiveness, for example, the charming sentence, written in age, 'I should very much like to see you again, but you would find a visit here very dull, for we feel very old and have no amusement, and lead a solitary life,'[37] or the much earlier passage: 'This letter is a most untidy one, but my mind is untidy with joy.'[38]

But Darwin, in writing, would have bestowed no thought or care on such qualities as these. He had a great discovery to give to the world. His one desire was to give it accurately, lucidly, and in a form that would convince, and it was his despair that he thought nature had not endowed him with the gifts for doing this. He envies the admirable literary skill of Huxley and Spencer and deplores his own inability to get his thoughts and ideas into a shape that would force mankind to read and understand them: 'I do not believe any man in England naturally writes so vile a style as I do.' [39]

Which is a gross exaggeration and belongs to the humility so manifest in other and more important matters. It is true that there are curious lapses from mere formal correctness, as in the rather attractive misuse of 'like,' which occasionally occurs: 'Few have observed like you have done.' [40] It is true, also, that Darwin had not the swift and eloquent vigor of Huxley, which has sometimes virile energy enough to make force of statement appear like truth of fact. But no one, I think, can read Darwin at all widely without getting to feel a singular charm in the absolute simplicity of his manner of expressing himself. To be sure, Huxley suggests that the very simplicity is sometimes misleading: 'A somewhat delusive simplicity of style, which tends to disguise the complexity and difficulty of the subject.' [41] But when so many writers make simple subjects difficult, it would surely be ungracious to complain of one who makes a difficult subject simple. As I have before suggested, Darwin's perfect candor, his absolute sincerity, his intense and obvious effort to have you think with him, seem to take the place of great literary qualities and to give his prose a revealing directness which is quite lacking to some who are more highly skilled.

Especially is this the case with the correspondence, where finish and technical perfection are of less importance than the power of spontaneous spiritual contact. In maintaining this contact there are few letter-writers who can surpass Darwin, and his four solid volumes, technical and scientific as they are, have a singular and persistent appeal to those who have a taste for that kind of writing.

As to his own personal enjoyment of literature, one form of it at least continued to attract him to the very last, and that was fiction. Relief from the strain of his scientific labors was best found in stories which distracted and absorbed: 'He was extremely fond of novels,' says his son, 'and I remember well the way in which he would anticipate the pleasure of having a novel read to him, as he lay down, or lighted his cigarette. He took a vivid interest both in plot and characters, and would on

145

no account know beforehand how a story finished; he considered looking at the end of a novel as a feminine vice.'[42] Darwin himself confirms this statement: 'Novels, which are works of the imagination, though not of a very high order, have been for years a wonderful relief and pleasure to me, and I often bless all novelists. A surprising number have been read aloud to me, and I like all if moderately good, and if they do not end unhappily — against which a law ought to be passed.'[43] He enjoyed Miss Austen, he adored Scott, and cites the Laird of Redgauntlet's facial peculiarity in the book on Expression. He did not like realism, even in the mild form practiced by George Eliot, and he wished things and people to be agreeable: 'A novel, according to my taste, does not come into the first class, unless it contains some person whom one can thoroughly love, and if a pretty woman, all the better.'[44]

But for the higher orders of literature, the loss was indubitable, and Darwin himself makes it very emphatic. He tells us that in his youth he enjoyed poetry. Shakespeare was his favorite reading. He read Thomson and Byron, and he got much pleasure from 'Paradise Lost': 'Formerly Milton's "Paradise Lost" had been my chief

favorite, and in my excursions during the voyage of
the *Beagle*, when I could take only a single volume,
I always chose Milton.'[45] The solid evidence of this
enjoyment is the frequent reference to poetical
reading in Darwin's books. Even in connection
with strictly scientific topics he is apt to introduce
some citation from the poets which not only proves
his point, but shows his familiarity.

Yet in later years all this poetical interest dis-
appeared, and Darwin bewails the disappearance
deeply. Shakespeare, who had touched and stirred
him, ceases to awaken any emotion, rings merely
hollow and empty: 'Now for many years I cannot
endure to read a line of poetry: I have tried lately
to read Shakespeare, and found it so intolerably
dull that it nauseated me.'[46]

A clever writer in the Popular Science Monthly
some years ago endeavored to prove that here, as
in other things, Darwin's humility much exaggerated his defects, and that his natural poetical
sympathy was greater than he recognized. This
writer urges Darwin's early enjoyment and his
constant, apt, and accurate quotation to establish the thesis: 'By his unconscious confession and
the evidence of his written works, his mind was
leavened with poetic feeling; all through his mature

life he is ready with quotation when the occasion calls; and the very poignancy of his regret for the loss of poetry witnesses to his poetic endowment.'[47] But the contention though ingenious, is exaggerated. Darwin's quick intelligence was interested in the substance of Shakespeare and Milton and other poets and prose writers. But it seems to me impossible that any one who had really felt the high stimulus of the splendor of Shakespeare's imagination could ever have lost it to any such extent as Darwin deplores with obvious sincerity. Sainte-Beuve had as wide and varied a scientific curiosity as Darwin's. But he said when he was well over fifty, 'I rarely write about poetry, precisely because I have loved it so much and because I still love it more than anything else.'[48] Goethe's old age was filled with scientific preoccupations, yet the glory of poetry was more to him than any possible science.

III

The most interesting point of all in connection with these æsthetic matters is that Darwin, for all his intimate contact with nature and all his scientific study, apparently did not feel much of the rapture and ecstasy that natural beauty affords

to many who have often little or no scientific knowledge. Here, more than in any other field, there is
of course a riot of convention and pretense, and
thousands prate of clouds and sunsets and bird-
song who have no more real feeling for these things
than they have for any other form of æsthetic development. Nevertheless, the ecstasy has been recorded and rendered by too many persons whose
gift of expression is as impressive as their sincerity
is indisputable, to be neglected or overlooked. It is
worth while to examine more closely into some
of the elements of this imaginative enjoyment of
the natural world.

To begin with, there is the delight of simple perception, the excitement, the inexplicable thrill
that goes with color and form and sound and
movement, with the nodding of a blossom and the
quiver of a butterfly, the

'Thoughts that do often lie too deep for tears.'

And no doubt this enjoyment is frequently too
subtle, too delicate, too elusive, too evanescent to
be put in words, and it comes to many who could
never find the words to convey it. Something of
its high intensity may be suggested by Cowper's
brief and poignant phrase: 'O! I could spend whole

days and moonlight nights in feeding upon a lovely prospect. My eyes drink the rivers as they flow.' [49]

The secret of the enjoyment must lie mainly in obscure processes of association, hints and suggestions of buried joy and sorrow, which go down deep into the roots of subconscious memory. But at any rate it is true that such enjoyment is bound up far more with simple scenes and home surroundings than with the remote or the picturesque or what Darwin so often refers to as the sublime. The hurrying tourist, who rushes about the world in search of some higher mountain or rougher glacier or wilder valley is not the one who feels the secret charm of nature, but rather he who strolls in lonely, quiet fields or woods that he has always known and loved. The return of violets in early spring, the song of thrushes in summer twilights, these are the things that bring tears, that come full charged with the weight of all that Cowper means when he writes of

'Scenes that soothed
Or charmed me young, no longer young I find
Still soothing and of power to charm me still.' [50]

And it is in this matter of association that the poets most of all help us. It is they who can disentangle the subtle threads of emotion and thought

that have twined themselves about the simple impressions of the natural world, and who in turn can
interweave a tissue of still more splendid imaginative glory with all our sight [and all our hearing.
It is Shakespeare with his

> 'Daffodils
> That come before the swallow dares, and take
> The winds of March with beauty.'

it is Keats, with his

> 'Tall oaks, branch-charmed by the earnest stars,'

or his,

> 'Fast-fading violets covered up in leaves,'

who store our souls with memories that vibrate at
the sight of daffodils and violets and stars.

And the imagination goes further yet, interpene-
trates the whole of nature, transforms it, makes it a
living, sentient unity, wholly unlike the dead multiplicity on which the scientist exercises his ingenious research. Take Emerson's 'Nature' and compare it with Darwin's book on Earthworms. The
Darwin has its fascination: it makes you long to
spend your days watching and testing and measuring the tiny creatures who are forever making over
the surface of the globe. But the Emerson trans-
fuses all this natural world with thought, with
creative human intelligence, dissolves it, moulds

it, re-creates it, tosses and turns it till it seems a ball and a trifle for the overmastering soul of man to produce or abolish as it will. Or again, with Wordsworth, there is the sense of animating life in nature, the dim, impersonal personality, which is for ever passing and repassing through the endless manifestations that are all the scientist can count or measure,

> 'A presence that disturbs me with the joy
> Of elevated thoughts.'

And as there is the sense of this profounder life in nature, this deeper, mysterious unity, back of all the varied shift and change, so there is the passionate desire to be at one with that unity, to lose one's miserable, insignificant, turbulent, tormenting I in that vast, illimitable, measureless All. There is the thirst of Shelley's 'Adonais':

> 'That sustaining love,
> Which, through the web of being blindly wove
> By man and beast and earth and air and sea,
> Burns bright or dim, as each are mirrors of
> The fire for which all thirst.'

There is Byron's cry:

> 'I live not in myself, but I become
> Portion of that about me, and to me
> High mountains are a feeling.'[51]

And with the realization that the longing cannot be satisfied, that we are forever imprisoned within the insuperable barriers of this petty I, from which there is no escape, comes a bitter revolt of despair, or a profound melancholy of questioning. It is Obermann, with his, 'There, in the peace of night, I questioned my uncertain destiny, and this inconceivable universe, which, containing everything yet does not contain my desires.'[52] Or, as an American contemporary has expressed the deep suggestion of the earnest stars: 'O Lyra, I have gazed at you, until I could not tell your brightness from my own eyes. I have gazed at you till my soul left my body, and circled with you through the stars; but there is something which I am and you are not, something which will not let me rest. . . .

'Infinite Intelligence! Infinite Beauty! Either make me what thou art, take me to thyself, or free me from this passion which I cannot gratify and cannot destroy. Make me as other men are, toilers and forgetters, seeking yesterday in to-day, and to-day in to-morrow, and illusion always; or fulfill for me the hope which the waters whisper, which I can feel throbbing forever in the heart of thy world.'

Of all this in Darwin nothing whatever, nothing, nothing. It may indeed be said that with nature, as with other things, many people have feelings and experiences that they do not express or try to express. But persons who cherish such experiences with the natural world usually have a more constant regard and interest for the expression of them in others than Darwin had. Any such melancholy or passionate longing as is suggested above one would of course not expect in him. There was no natural melancholy in his temperament. He was depressed and discouraged when things went badly, yet in the main his disposition was even and serene. But his enjoyment of natural scenes and objects, which is indisputable and proved by his own testimony and that of others, would seem to have been generally of a rather superficial character, and certainly not to have partaken of the nature of passion. How far, far different is his touch from that of Lucretius, for example.

Darwin enjoyed picturesque surroundings and novel experiences. He enjoyed the beauty of flowers, their color and shape. His son's account of this is very charming: 'I used to like to hear him admire the beauty of a flower; it was a kind of gratitude to the flower itself, and a personal love for its delicate form and color. I seem to remember him gently touching a flower he delighted in; it was the same simple admiration that a child might have.'[53] Occasionally, also, there are scattered

154

hints which seem to suggest a deeper feeling. There is the description of the hour in Moor Park: 'At last I fell asleep on the grass, and awoke with a chorus of birds singing around me, and squirrels running up the trees, and some woodpeckers laughing, and it was as pleasant and rural a scene as ever I saw, and I did not care one penny how any of the beasts or birds had been formed.'[54] Yet even here, 'as pleasant and rural a scene as ever I saw,' is the eighteenth century, not the nineteenth. There is the still intenser bit in the 'Beagle': 'Neither plant nor bird, excepting a few condors wheeling around the higher pinnacles, distracted my attention from the inanimate mass. I felt glad that I was alone: it was like watching a thunderstorm, or hearing in full orchestra a chorus of the Messiah.'[55] And there is the striking touch in the early letter to Henslow: 'The delight of sitting on a decaying trunk amidst the quiet gloom of the forest is unspeakable, and never to be forgotten,'[56] which at least suggests Obermann in the Forest of Fontainebleau.

But these rare and scattered intimations serve only to bring out the different nature of the habitual attitude, and it is clear enough that such æsthetic element as there was gradually faded in the growing absorption of the scientific ardor. It cannot be denied that in the main Darwin's interest in nature was intellectual, not emotional.

IV

As with sociology and with æsthetic experience, so, and even more, with God and the things of God, Darwin's limitations are profoundly interesting, and if the loss was less, because there was less to lose, it was nevertheless, in all its aspects significant. Here again, as with æsthetic emotion, it must be remembered that men do not utter all they feel, and those who feel most sometimes utter least. But it so happens that circumstances obliged Darwin to be very explicit about his religious views and experiences, so that we are justified in assuming that we have access to pretty much all there was.

It must never be forgotten that Darwin grew up in the thoroughly conventional atmosphere of the English Church. Neither his father nor his grandfather was an active believer, but the immense tradition of staid decorum, from which the English upper middle class rarely escapes, was all about his boyhood, and left an indelible mark on it. To appreciate how haunting and oppressive the atmo-

sphere was, one should read 'A Century of Family
Letters,' edited by Darwin's daughter. The flavor
of established religious propriety is so overwhelm-
ing that one wonders how Darwin could ever have
shaken himself intellectually free from it.

Mrs. Darwin was a wise and a charming woman,
and she was invaluable to her husband, but, oh, she
was English. She took a proper wifely interest in
Darwin's scientific adventures, and was sometimes
of assistance to him. She had her anxieties about
the animosity of his critics and also about the drift
of his speculations, and her daughter implies that
in later years these speculations effected a change
in the mother's religious beliefs.[57] But I relish very
much this lovely passage of solicitude for the husband's eternal welfare, written in the year of the
publication of the 'Origin': 'I am sure you know I
love you well enough to believe that I mind your
sufferings, nearly as much as I should my own, and I
find the only relief to my own mind is to take it as
from God's hand, and to try to believe that all
suffering and illness is meant to help us to exalt our
minds and to look forward with hope to a future
state. When I see your patience, deep compassion
for others, self-command, and above all gratitude
for the smallest thing done to help you, I cannot

157

help longing that these precious feelings should be offered to Heaven for the sake of your daily happiness.'[58] Also, Mrs. Darwin was a careful observer of that augustly hideous institution, the Victorian Sunday: 'I remember she persuaded me,' writes a reminiscent relative, 'to refuse any invitation from the neighbors that involved using the carriage on that day, and it was a question in her own mind whether she might rightly embroider, knit, or play patience.'[59] It strikes me as peculiarly delightful that the Sabbath should be treated with such reverence in the house of one who was to do more than any one else to smash the God of the Sabbath altogether.

So it is evident that Darwin grew up with a strong religious habit. There was even serious talk of his entering the church, till his hopeless lack of vocation made it clearly impossible. The net of religious inheritance and circumstance was woven closely about him and in the early days he recognized himself as in general orthodox enough. I like particularly the reply he made to his Catholic friends in South America, who conjured him to see the light: 'Why do you not become a Christian — for our religion is certain?' 'I assured them I was a sort of Christian.'[60] A sort of Christian! Isn't that charmingly characteristic? You can imagine millions of fanatics to-day howling, 'What sort of Christian?'

One thing at least is certain: Darwin never was cynical or mocking in his attitude toward religion. Without the least trace of affectation or cant, he always spoke of the church and the clergy and religious practice with respect, and with the same gentle tolerance that he displayed towards those who differed from him in any line. Peculiarly significant in this regard are his references to the missionaries with whom he came into contact on his southern voyage. He was at first disposed to speak of them without enthusiasm, to say the least, and Admiral Sullivan, who was with him on the Beagle, tells of his scepticism about missionary work, 'his conviction that it was utterly useless to send missionaries to such a set of savages as the Fuegians.'[61] Many years later Darwin was entirely converted, and, as usual, did not hesitate to say so: 'He wrote me that he had been wrong and I right in our estimates of the native character, and the possibility of doing them good through missionaries; and he requested me to forward to the Society an enclosed cheque for £5, as a testimony of the interest he took in their good work.'[62] Other passages could be adduced to the same effect.

And the religious training and the constant presence of high-minded and earnest living and meaning people about him had established in Darwin a secure habit of morals and a vivid activity of conscience. He might subject the moral habit in theory to cold analysis, 'The moral nature of man has reached its present standard, partly through the advancement of his reasoning powers and consequently of a just public opinion, but especially from his sympathies having been rendered more tender and widely diffused through the effects of habit, example, instruction, and reflection.'[63] But the analysis did not in the least affect his own personal instinct of right and upright living.

It is not only that there is no appearance or record of irregularity of conduct of any kind. But, much more than this, there is repeated evidence of the nicest scrupulousness and a tender conscience which would not be surpassed in the most devout and anxious Christian. It was perhaps 'a sort of Christian,' but assuredly not a bad sort, who, as I have before mentioned, got up in the middle of the night to correct a fancied misstatement, not about a scientific fact, but about an æsthetic experience.[64] And a clerical friend records a similar incident, equally striking: 'On one occasion, when a parish

meeting had been held on some disputed point of
no great importance, I was surprised by a visit
from Mr. Darwin at night. He came to say that,
thinking over the debate, though what he had said
was quite accurate, he thought I might have drawn
an erroneous conclusion, and he would not sleep
till he had explained it.' [65] With the members of his
own family there was the same scrupulous, tender
anxiety not to do or say anything unjust or unkind.
After some quite warrantable and reasonable outburst of indignation over the levity of one of his
sons, 'The next morning at seven o'clock he came
to my bedroom and said how sorry he was that he
had been so angry and that he had not been able to
sleep; and with a few kind words he left me.' [66]
This 'sort of Christian' is perhaps not even yet so
common as might be wished.

On the other hand, when we come to the more
intimate, personal aspects of the religious life,
Darwin's record appears to be largely negative, and
what earlier traces there are gradually disappear.
Take prayer. Here again, in the study of Expression, we have the scientific analysis, of prayer as an
attitude at any rate: 'Hence it is not probable that
either the uplifting of the eyes or the joining of the
open hands under the influence of devotional

feelings, are innate or truly expressive actions, and this could hardly have been expected, for it is very doubtful whether feelings, such as we should rank as devotional, affected the hearts of men, whilst they remained during past ages in an uncivilized condition.'[67] Also, there are other occasional references to the external aspects of religious petition, as in the Beagle Journal: 'He prayed as a Christian should do, with fitting reverence, and without the fear of ridicule or any ostentation of piety.'[68]

But to prayer as a personal experience I find only one single allusion. When Darwin was a boy, he was a good runner, often took part in races, and was often successful. His explanation of his success at that time is interesting: 'When in doubt I prayed earnestly to God to help me, and I well remember that I attributed my success to my prayers and not to my quick running, and marveled how generally I was aided.'[69] This recalls the youthful experience of Moody, who was caught under a fence rail and could not move, but put up earnest prayers to God, and then was able to lift the rail quite easily.

Prayer played a very different part in Moody's later life from what it did in Darwin's, so far as any tangible evidence goes. It is true that probably a good many men pray whom one would never suspect of doing so. I had an old friend, who had been brought up devoutly but had been a Unitarian for years, rarely going to church, apparently indifferent to religion, and discussing speculative, ultimate problems with annihilating freedom. Yet he told me, in an outburst of confidence, that every night, when he went to bed, he repeated, in substance, if not in words, the prayers that he had learned at his mother's knee. 'I don't know what it means,' he said; 'I don't know whether there is a God, or whether He hears me, or what I want of Him; but I pray.' And I, who had not prayed for thirty years, heard him with amazement. Nevertheless, I do not believe that Darwin repeated 'Now I lay me' to the end, or prayed for triumph with evolution as he had prayed for triumph in the foot-race.

The question of a future life seems to have had as little actuality for Darwin as that of prayer, and we have more explicit evidence on the point, because correspondents were always writing for a statement of his beliefs. He never committed himself to any complete assertion of disbelief. On the contrary, he is quite ready to admit some forcible positive arguments: 'Believing as I do that man in the distant future will be a far more perfect creature than he now is, it is an intolerable thought that he and all other sentient beings are doomed to complete annihilation after such long-continued slow progress. To those who fully admit the immortality of the human soul, the destruction of our world will not appear so dreadful.'[70] Yet the difficulties seem insuperable, and he is hardly able to accept any definite belief: 'Many persons seem to make themselves quite easy about immortality . . . by intuition; and I suppose I must differ from such persons because I do not feel any innate conviction upon such points.'[71]

The supreme test as to the future is the death of those we love and the thought of our own death. In 1851 Darwin lost a little daughter whom he loved tenderly. His intimate letters at that time have affectionate and pathetic references to her; but there is not one word in them to indicate the slightest hope of ever meeting her again. When he himself was close to the end, mentally clear but with no prospect of recovery, his calm words were: 'I am not the least afraid of death.'[72]

As to the question of God, Darwin's statements are as elaborate as in regard to immortality, and for the same reason, because eager inquirers were

determined to find out where he stood. In early
life, while he still believed in the theory of special
creations, he accepted the deistic view without
hesitation: 'Many years ago, when I was collecting
facts for the "Origin," my belief in what is called
a personal God was as firm as that of Dr. Pusey
himself.'[73] As the years went on, the working out
of his theories involved a profound change, but
still he never at any time admitted an absolute disbelief or a militant atheism. He goes over and over
the old, old arguments. How could an omnipotent
God, who desired the good of all his creatures, in-
flict upon the travailing creation such an infinity of
misery? Again, there is the puzzle of design and
providential interference. He is reluctant to believe that this vast and ordered whole came together by mere chance; yet he debates with Asa
Gray the possible providence in the fall of a spar-
row: 'An innocent and good man stands under a
tree and is killed by a flash of lightning. Do you
believe (and I really should like to hear) that God
designedly killed this man? Many or most persons
do believe this; I can't and don't. If you believe
so, do you believe that when a swallow snaps up
a gnat that God designed that that particular swallow should snap up that particular gnat at that

CHAPTER V

DARWIN: THE LOVER

I

IF Darwin was not conspicuous as a lover of God, he was at least notable in every way as one who loved his fellow men. He liked to meet people, liked to talk with them, liked to have them about him. He was interested in humanity, enjoyed the contact of it, and felt in others the warm throb of a heart that beat as kindly and sympathetically as his own. Men, women, and children were drawn to him and recognized a friend.

Of his personal appearance the chief impression that comes to us is naturally in age. He was tall and powerfully built, and in his youth must have been attractive to look at, though there is no definite record of this. In later years his aspect was dignified without being severe. 'His face is massive,' writes Norton to Ruskin, with 'little beauty of feature, but much of expression.'[1] What seems to have chiefly impressed observers was the eyes and the look in them. Professor Osborn says: 'The impression of Darwin's bluish-gray eyes, deep-set under overhanging brows, was that they were the eyes of a man who could survey all nature.'[2] And Bryce agrees: 'The feature which struck one most was the projecting brow with its bushy eyebrows, and deep beneath it the large gray-blue eyes with their clear and steady look. It was an alert look, as of one accustomed to observing keenly, yet it was also calm and reflective. There was a pleasant smile which came and passed readily, but the chief impression made by the face was that of tranquil, patient thoughtfulness, as of one whose mind had long been accustomed to fix itself upon serious problems.'[3]

There is general testimony as to Darwin's ready hospitality and eager kindliness in greeting all those who came into his household. There was no reserve or assumption of dignity, but a perfectly natural and cordial desire and disposition to make every one feel at home. I do not know any more impressive witness to this charm of manner than Leslie Stephen, who was certainly not a man to be unduly carried away. Stephen speaks of 'the charm which no one to whom I have ever spoken failed to perceive in his presence and in his writings.'[4] And he elsewhere dwells upon it more elaborately: 'He was in town for a few days and most kindly called upon me. You may believe that I was he inclined to witty flings or brilliant repartee. His mind worked too slowly for a rapid-fire exchange of this sort. It was only occasionally that he hit out at a promising interlocutor, as when he remarked to Lady Derby, who had been describing her remarkable peculiarities of vision, 'Ah, Lady Derby, how I should like to dissect you.'[9] Above all, he had no taste for the satirical or bitter, and it was only under extreme provocation that he could write to Huxley: 'God bless you! — get well, be idle, and always reverence a bishop.'[10]

But he was full of genial, kindly fun, and was ready to see the laughable side of little incidents and even great. He laughed heartily and frequently and with an infectious gayety and buoyancy. He liked merry and humorous talk, with plenty of anecdote and sparkle, and he was ready to chaff and joke his friends and to take the same sort of thing himself. He was even willing to find a comic side in the sacred subject of natural selection and to turn his own deepest interests into matter for smiles when the occasion was suitable. Thus he writes to Lubbock, of his son: 'See what it is to be well trained. Horace said to me yesterday, "If every one would kill adders they would come to sting less." I answered, "Of course they would,

for there would be fewer." He replied indignantly:
"I did not mean that; but the timid adders which
run away would be saved, and in time they would
never sting at all." Natural selection of cowards!' [11]

In Darwin's later years he might of course have
been crowded with social engagements all the time.
Everybody wanted to see him, to know him, to talk
with him, to entertain him. The preoccupation of
his work and the limitations of his health made any
such social activity impossible, and it is not likely
that he greatly missed it. Yet, wherever he went,
he was welcome, his society was appreciated, not
only for his reputation, but for itself, and when he
could get about, it evidently gave him pleasure:
'I dined with Bell at the Linnean Club, and liked
my dinner . . . dining out is such a novelty to me that
I enjoyed it.' [12] At an earlier period, when there
was more strength to spare for such diversions, he
entered into them with hearty enthusiasm, and
even, it appears, with a thorough rollicking zest.
When he settled himself in Cambridge, after his
return from the Beagle voyage, he complained
that the only trouble was that life was too pleasant and some agreeable party every evening made
morning labor rather difficult. [13] And of the mis-
cellaneous social gatherings of still earlier days he

writes: 'We used often to dine together in the evening, though these dinners often included men of a higher stamp, and we sometimes drank too much, with jolly singing and playing at cards afterwards. I know that I ought to feel ashamed of days and evenings thus spent, but as some of my friends were very pleasant, and we were all in the highest spirits, I cannot help looking back to these times with much pleasure.' [14]

In the matter of sports and diversions Darwin's tastes seem to have run rather to those which are not in their nature social, though what attracted him was the character of the sports themselves, and not the element of solitude. In his youth he was passionately fond of outdoor sport, of fishing and hunting. He had a keen love for angling, he says, and would sit for hours watching his float in some solitary pool or stream, though when some one told him that he could kill the angle worms with salt and water instead of spitting them on the hook, it was a great relief to his feelings. [15] He was especially eager with a gun, and long before he took the slightest interest in the scientific study of birds, he liked to kill them. He tells us that the killing of his first snipe excited him so much that he trembled till it was difficult to reload his gun.

Even after his scientific interest had begun to develop, he dropped every vestige of it in the shooting season: 'at that time I should have thought myself mad to give up the first days of partridge-shooting for geology or any other science.'[16]

He became an excellent shot and, as his son says, had all his life a remarkable power of coördinating his movements, so that he was not only accurate with a gun, but in throwing, and after he was a grown man, simply to test his skill, he threw a marble at a cross-beak and killed it: 'He was so unhappy at having uselessly killed the cross-beak that he did not mention it for years, and then explained that he should never have thrown at it if he had not felt sure that his old skill had gone from him.'[17] Perhaps the most striking witness to the depth of Darwin's passion for these field sports is the unusually harsh remark of his father who loved his son and was deeply beloved by him: 'You care for nothing but shooting, dogs, and rat-catching, and will be a disgrace to yourself and all your family.'[18] Which is not the first case of imperfect prevision on the part of a father, nor the last.

Of games that are more essentially social, there is no indication that Darwin was an ardent practitioner. When he was at school he played 'bat-fives,'[19] but there is no mention of football or cricket. In describing his personal tastes in later years, he speaks of cards with something of contempt: 'Have not played for many years, but I am sure I should not remember.'[20] His tone about them in 1842, however, is quite different: 'This walk was rather too much for me, and I was dull till whist, which I enjoyed beyond measure.'[21] In 1859, the year of the 'Origin,' he set up a billiard-table, 'and I find it does me a deal of good, and drives the horrid species out of my head.'[22] But his special pleasure in the game line was backgammon, which he played with Mrs. Darwin, year after year, keeping a score of victories and defeats, getting or pretending to be, greatly excited over his failures and even indignant at his antagonist's good-fortune. In 1875 he wrote to Asa Gray: 'Pray give our very kind remembrances to Mrs. Gray. I know that she likes to hear men boasting, it refreshes them so much. Now the tally with my wife in backgammon stands thus: she, poor creature, has won only 2490 games, whilst I have won, hurrah, hurrah, 2795 games.'[23]

But through it all Darwin's humanity is evident everywhere. He loved his fellow-creatures, loved to mix with them, and to have them care for him, and his interest went far deeper than a mere, though absorbing, curiosity as to their animal origin.

II

The drawback to Darwin's social life, as to his power of work, was in the limitations of health, and if we would fully appreciate not only the heroism of his achievement, but the charm of his character, we must understand how great and far-reaching those limitations were. The natural strength and vigor of his sturdily constructed frame endured through youth and in the main through the Beagle voyage, in spite of the persistent sea-sickness; but from shortly after his return to England on, his life was nothing but a more or less relieved and varying chronic invalidism.

The effect of this upon his scientific labors I have indicated earlier. It hampered them at every step. He could work but a few hours in the morning and after that the constant effort and lesson was in the endeavor to forget; 'It is so weariful, killing the whole afternoon, after 12 o'clock, doing nothing whatever.'[24] A piece of investigation, which required perhaps the most nice and constant watchfulness, had to be abandoned in the middle, because recurring and increasing symptoms abso-

symptoms and the conditions to conjecture with great definiteness, though the] enlarged medical knowledge of to-day might interpret matters that were then obscure. There was sometimes a disposition to attribute the whole recurring misery of later years to the Beagle sea-sickness. But Darwin himself rejected this explanation and his son points out that the settled illness came on only gradually some years after his return.[28] Darwin believed that his bad health was due 'to the hereditary fault which came out as gout in some of the past generations.'[29] The specialists of that day were quite at sea. 'Dr. Brinton has been here,' says Darwin; 'he does not believe my brain or heart primarily affected, but I have been so steadily going down hill, I cannot help doubting whether I can ever crawl a little uphill again.'[30] It is amusing to see how later speculators have exercised their wits upon the case. Dr. George M. Gould, in his brilliant 'Biographic Clinics,' grouped Darwin with Huxley, Tennyson, Browning, and a dozen others, as a victim of eye-strain, and believed all his trouble could have been disposed of by properly refracting glasses. With the development of glandular theories, Darwin's thyroid, pituitary, and adrenal secretions have been set down as excessive or deficient. With his build, he would certainly have been a promising subject for the experiments of the orthopædist, while the dietitian would have prescribed unlimited spinach and carrots, the osteopath would have discovered disastrous subluxations in the spine, and the psycho-analyst would see the foundation of the whole trouble in disordered complexes. And all of them would have some symptomatic justification, and all of them would have been eager to work over the poor man, as they have done over many another such, with mountains of expectation and promise and outlay, and too often a pitiful mouse of result.

Fortunately, or unfortunately, the specialist was not quite so rampant in Darwin's day, and while later scientific developments might, or might not, have cured him, he escaped a good deal of unprofitable discomfort. The water cure was fashionable at that time and he was duly put through it, with some annoyance, and perhaps with a little improvement: 'One most singular effect of the treatment is that it induces in most people, and eminently in my case, the most complete stagnation of mind. I have ceased to think even of barnacles.'[31]

But pending the discovery of some miraculous cure, the only help seemed to be in persistent care, self-control, and discipline. It was necessary to be careful as to eating, and here Darwin appears to have been generally abstemious, though he had a taste for sweets, which he sometimes indulged with humorous excuses and a clear prevision of the bad results that were likely to follow, and did. As to alcohol, even in his earlier years when boisterous excess in drinking was common enough, Darwin was not much inclined to anything of the sort. He does indeed tell of gay supper-parties, where too much wine was drunk. His son records his confession, in answer to a query as to early habits, that 'he was ashamed to say he had once drunk too much at Cambridge.' [32] And Grant Duff mentions a curious remark, which seems well vouched for but is hard to believe: 'Hooker, who is staying here, amused us by saying that Darwin had told him that he had got drunk three times in early life, and thought intoxication the greatest of all pleasures.' [33] Whether he thought so or not, he did not often indulge in it. And as he grew older, he abandoned wine almost entirely, so that when she was engaged his future wife could write: 'I don't think it of as much consequence as she does that Charles drinks no wine, but I think it a pleasant thing.' [34] He smoked cigarettes more or less, and found them restful, but he certainly did not overdo the habit. His favorite indulgence was snuff-taking, which was given up and renewed much after the fashion of Lamb's tobacco. Of his efforts in this direction he writes, with humor: 'I am personally in a state of utmost confusion also, for my cruel wife has persuaded me to leave off snuff for a month; and I am most lethargic, stupid, and melancholy in consequence.' [35]

The chief element in Darwin's care of his health, however, was persistent rest. All his days were systematically planned, the few hours that could be given to it set apart for work, and the rest devoted to some form of relaxation or needed repose. There were long nights, if not for sleep, at least for physical tranquillity, and there were afternoons and evenings spent largely on the sofa, in chat or in listening to music or to stories of purely diverting quality. Any interruption of this carefully arranged schedule was avoided, if possible, and almost always had to be paid for. Thus, by persistent, systematic, rigid self-control, and by sacrificing days and months and years to a comparatively tedious indolence, Darwin gained the few hours that were essential for the work that shook the world.

In one respect he was extremely fortunate. If he was hampered by ill-health, he at least had ample means to make that ill-health as tolerable as possible. He did not know the misery of having to support yourself and your family and being physically unable to do it. Without wholly endorsing the sarcastic remark of Butler, 'The worst thing that can happen to a man is to lose his money, the next his health, and the third his reputation,' one can see some truth in it, especially when the possession of money serves to make the loss of health more endurable. Darwin's father was very successful financially. He provided for all his children in the most liberal fashion during his life, and left them in comfortable circumstances after his death, and Darwin often refers to this with gratitude and appreciation. The son seems to have had abundant means to keep up a considerable establishment, to educate and provide for his own large family, to indulge in general benefaction, and to do if not all he wished, at least a great deal in the way of scientific investigation and experiment.

In later years a considerable income from the published books was naturally added to the supply that was inherited. Darwin was proud of his earning in this way, and he had reason to be, although he could hardly boast of such returns as were received by his contemporary Trollope. One is chiefly impressed, however, with his extreme anxiety that others should be treated fairly, and that no one should suffer by his gains. Thus he writes to his publisher, in a tone which publishers will I think recognize as not usual: 'You are really too generous about the, to me, scandalously heavy corrections. Are you acting fairly towards yourself? Would it not be better at least to share the £72 8s? I shall be fully satisfied, for I had no business to send, though quite unintentionally and unexpectedly, such badly composed MS to the printers.'[36]

One of the consequences of Darwin's delicate health was, that he was more or less anxious about money. When you can count on your physical strength for fighting circumstance, you can float cheerfully out into the world and let your daily support come where you can get it. But if you are weak, crippled, and hampered, if you are absolutely dependent upon the comforts which others merely enjoy but can do without, you look with dread upon the possibility of losing what alone assures you of the indispensable. Darwin was not altogether free from this feeling, and his son tells us that he was haunted by the fear that his children would not have health to earn their own living yet might be obliged to do so.[37] In consequence he was always thoughtful and careful in money matters. He looked after his investments with shrewd intelligence, and respected the faculty of making money and keeping it. He was not above saving a penny where it could be done, and especially he was exact and systematic about his expenditure. His biographer says that 'he kept accounts with great care, classifying them, and balancing at the end of the year like a merchant. I remember the quick way in which he would reach out for his account book to enter each check paid, as though he were in a hurry to get it entered before he had forgotten it.'[38] An interesting contradiction to this financial exactitude and to Darwin's ordinary habits of accuracy is his inveterate carelessness in not dating or not fully dating his letters.

The financial exactitude and anxiety do not for a moment imply that he was not liberal and generous in the highest degree, as perhaps the wisest, and even the largest generosity, comes with such prevision and forethought. He spent freely on his current living, and he was particularly considerate, not only in giving to his family, but in the

manner of giving, which sometimes seems to count
for even more. His son speaks of his thoughtful
kindness in attending to financial arrangements,
and emphasizes his generosity in paying college
debts, 'making it almost seem a virtue in me to
have told him of them.'[39] Nor was the generosity
confined to his family. It was broad and luminous
in its working, and there are constant references
to the causes to which Darwin sent his check, with
no ostentation, but with the earnest desire to do
good. His limitations of strength made it difficult
for him to go about largely in his home neighbor-
hood, but the poor people knew him and loved him,
and he was ready and glad to assist them when
possible. As Bryce says, 'he was a kind and helpful neighbor to the humble folk who lived round
him at Down.'[40] Especially he was glad to give not
only his time and his limited strength, but his
money, to aiding those who were doing scientific
work of any sort. And in brief, in this connection
of general kindliness it is worth while to note the
remark of the devout old woman who was told that
Darwin would go to hell for his wicked doctrines
and answered: 'God Almighty can't afford to do
without so good a man.'[41]

III

It was a natural consequence of invalidism that Darwin's social habits and inclinations were conspicuous in the domestic circle. He seems to have been kindly and considerate with every one in the household, and the servants liked him, though they were sometimes puzzled by his pursuits, as when a gardener remarked that he thought Mr. Darwin would be better if he had more to do. It was very rare that he got out of temper with those who worked for him, and he dreaded having to scold any one because he knew that he was liable to say more than he meant.[42] His son tells us, 'when I overheard a servant being scolded, and my father speaking angrily, it impressed me as an appalling circumstance.'[43] In general his manner was courteous and conciliatory and he appeared more as if he were asking a favor than giving an order. When he was overcome by illness, in the very last days, he refused to allow a neighbor's butler either to call a cab or to accompany him home, as he was unwilling to give so much trouble.

Darwin's extreme love for all domestic animals I have already indicated negatively in dealing with his dislike of cruelty and ill-treatment, but the love was always positive and showed itself in constant interest and attention and care. One instance of much regretted sin in this regard is amusingly recorded in the Autobiographical Sketch: 'Once as a very little boy whilst at the day school, or before that time, I acted cruelly, for I beat a puppy, I believe, simply from enjoying the sense of power; but the beating could not have been severe, for the puppy did not howl, of which I feel sure, as the spot was near the house. This act lay heavily on my conscience, as is shown by my remembering the exact spot where the crime was committed.'[44] But the crime was not repeated in later life. Even to the pigeons, which he raised for purposes of scientific investigation Darwin became greatly attached: 'I love them to that extent,' he says, 'that I cannot bear to kill and skeletonize them.'[45] His dogs were matter of interest and delight and intense affection to him always. And dogs of all kinds seemed to be drawn to him. As a young man his sister's pets would follow him instead of her, and with the dog of a friend at Cambridge it was the same. Dogs were not only the subject of his minute observations for the study of expression, they were his companions in his daily walks and his intimate friends.

For all the members of his family Darwin's

affection was deep, solid, and lasting. The tenderness with which he regarded his father's memory is, it seems to me, somewhat unusual: 'I do not think any one could love a father much more than I did mine, and I do not believe three or four days ever pass without my still thinking of him.'[46] The tenderness shows especially in the long sketch of his father's character, which is far less qualified with critical comments than one would expect from Darwin's naturally analytical disposition, and always where his affection was concerned the analysis seemed to drop somewhat into abeyance. His references to his brothers and sisters also show in simple earnestness how much they meant in his life.

Naturally the most prominent figure in the domestic circle is Mrs. Darwin, and the depth and endurance of Darwin's affection for her are everywhere evident. There is no record or intimation of any earlier attachment or love-affair. Very likely there were such, but neither Darwin nor his biographers give any hint of them. We have seen that he liked pretty women in novels, and occasionally in his books he makes some reference to feminine attraction. His daughter tells us that 'He was often in love with the heroines of the many novels

EMMA DARWIN AT THIRTY-ONE

that were read to him, and used always to maintain both in books and real life that a touch of affectation was necessary to complete the charm of a pretty woman.'[47] The daughter finds it difficult to understand what this means, as her father had such a horror of affectation in general. It seems to me at any rate to mean that he did not take love-making very seriously, and there is certainly no sign that it ever much disturbed his life.

Even when he was engaged, his love for Emma Wedgwood does not seem to have been of the kind that stings and burns. His letters to her that have been printed are gentle, considerate, and sympathetic: they exhibit none of the torments that self-doubting and self-spurring and ardently exultant passion are inclined to. In the most attractive of them he writes: 'Excuse this much egotism — I give it you because I think you will humanize me, and soon teach me there is greater happiness than building theories and accumulating facts in silence and solitude. My own dearest Emma, I earnestly pray, you may never regret the great, and I will add very good deed, you are to perform on the Tuesday.'[48] And he adds playfully: 'I want practice in ill-treating the female sex — I did not observe Lyell had any compunction; I hope to harden my conscience in time: few husbands seem to find it difficult to effect this.'[49] Everything is right and as it should be. But the tone is not that of some love-letters I have seen, and this is the more notable, considering the extraordinary frankness and directness of Darwin's correspondence generally.

But if Darwin's conjugal attachment did not begin with violence and high-wrought passion, it continued and deepened and strengthened with broad sunny richness to the end of his life. And this was just as true, although Mrs. Darwin had no particular affection for his scientific pursuits. I have said elsewhere that she assisted him, and in his work as in everything else she was eager to do her wifely duty and help where she could. But she had no love for the work in itself, and her daughter remarks that though in the beginning she had resolved to enter into her husband's tastes, she found it impossible. 'He used to tell how during some lecture at the British Association he said to her, "I am afraid this is very wearisome to you," to which she quietly answered, "Not more than all the rest."'[50] And in writing to Lubbock he makes gentle fun of her indifference: 'Of course you will publish an account of [your discovery]. You will then say whether the insect can fly well through the air. My wife asked, "How did he find that it stayed four hours under water without breathing?" I answered at once: "Mrs. Lubbock sat four hours watching." I wonder whether I am right.'[51]

But Darwin did not demand that the woman he loved should share all his professional ardor. He loved her for other things, which he found in her sufficingly and inexhaustibly, for her patience, her thoughtfulness, her quick and vivacious sympathy and understanding, and the general charm of her character. In a passage of his Autobiography not published till after Mrs. Darwin's death he said of her: 'She has been my greatest blessing . . . I do not believe she has ever missed an opportunity of doing a kind action to any one near her. I marvel at my good fortune that she, so infinitely my superior in every moral quality, consented to be my wife.'[52] And in the ardor of indiscriminating affection he adds a note of eulogy which could not perhaps be justly written by any one of any one: 'I can declare that in my whole life I have never heard her utter one word I would rather have been unsaid.'[53]

Darwin's constant ill-health gave a peculiar quality of intimate dependence to his relation to her whose care did most to make the ill-health tolerable, and Darwin's son bears emphatic witness to the unfailing devotion, thoughtfulness, and efficacy of that care. 'For all the latter years of his life she never left him for a night; and her days were so planned that all his resting hours might be shared with her.'⁵⁴ [54] Only those who have known the situation can fully appreciate the restraint and constraint involved in such chronic invalidism, not only for the one who bears, but perhaps still more for the one who must watch, and sympathize, and shield, and protect, and as far as possible keep off the pressure and strain of the crowding, noisy, bustling, indifferent world.

It is true that Mrs. Darwin was spared some of the more trying elements of such invalidism. It too often carries with it impatience, irritability, ill-temper, complaint, or at any rate a moody depression which refuses to be comforted or dissipated. We have seen that Darwin confessed to some quickness of temper in youth, but there appears to have been no sign of it whatever during the years of illness. He was not only gentle and considerate, he was almost always cheerful, even gay, and relished having love and cheerfulness and gayety about him. As Mrs. Darwin charmingly puts it: 'It is a great happiness to me when Charles is most unwell that he continues just as sociable as ever, and is not like the rest of the Darwins, who will not say how they really are; but he always tells me how he feels and never wants to be alone, but continues just as warmly affectionate as ever, so that I feel I am a comfort to him.'[55] Nor is there any sign of growing selfishness. An invalid must in a measure protect himself, he must make certain demands, and in many cases these necessary demands tend to grow into the inconsiderate and the morbidly engrossing. It does not seem to have been so with Darwin. He thought of others before himself, and kept his own needs and his own discomforts as much in the background as possible.

Nevertheless, he was an invalid, and his wife was well and vigorous, and could have mingled largely and freely with the world, and would doubtless have enjoyed it. Instead, she gave her life to him, and he fully appreciated the beauty and the constancy of her devotion. As his son says: 'In her presence he found his happiness, and through her his life — which might have been overshadowed by gloom — became one of content and quiet gladness.'[56] But I think I feel most the human depth of the broken notes which Mrs. Darwin herself entered, recording the very last hours and words of her husband's life: 'I will only put down his words

afterwards — "I am not the least afraid of death."
"Remember what a good wife you have been to
me." "Tell all my children to remember how good
they have been to me." After the worst of the distress he said, "I was so sorry for you, but I could
not help you." Then, "I am glad of it," when told
I was lying down. "Don't call her; I don't want
her." Said often, "It's almost worth while to be
sick to be nursed by you." ' [57]

In his relations with his children Darwin is quite
as winning as in that with his wife. He had a huge
household of them, ten in all, boys and girls. His
home-keeping habits brought him closely into
contact with them, and he loved them, and they
loved him. It is true that he appreciates the conflict of family cares with the one all-absorbing pursuit of life, appreciates it and states it with almost
tragic force and compactness: 'Children are one's
greatest happiness, but often and often a still
greater misery. A man of science ought to have
none — perhaps not a wife; for then there would be
nothing in this wide world worth caring for, and a
man might (whether he could is another question)
work away like a Trojan.' [58] With which it is interesting to compare the similar complaint of an
equally devoted father, Thomas Moore: 'My anx-

iety about these children almost embitters all my enjoyment of them.'[59]

But the anxiety arose simply from an excess of thought and care and fondness, and assuredly few fathers have been more devoted than Darwin was. There is no sign whatever that he was severe or harsh in his discipline. His son says that he never spoke an angry word to one of his children in his life. Yet he somehow managed to get things done as he wished: 'I am certain that it never entered our heads to disobey him.'[60] The ease and comradeship with which he worked appear in one anecdote told by Francis: 'He came into the drawing-room and found Leonard dancing about on the sofa, which was forbidden, for the sake of the springs, and said, "Oh, Lenny, Lenny, that's against all rules," and received for answer, "Then, I think you'd better go out of the room."'[61] But I do not imagine that Leonard did any more dancing.

The basis of all discipline was sympathy and understanding, just as these were the basis of Darwin's dealings with his fellow-scientists; and in his respect for his children's personality and individuality he seems to have anticipated the ideas of a later age. His daughter says: 'Another characteristic of his treatment of his children was his respect for their liberty, and for their personality. . . . Our father and mother would not even wish to know what we were doing or thinking unless we wished to tell. He always made us feel that we were each of us creatures whose opinions and thoughts were valuable to him, so that whatever there was best in us came out in the sunshine of his presence.'[62]

We have already seen what care Darwin took at all times in regard to his childrens' comfort in money matters. There was the same solicitude in all their affairs, as to their education, their conduct, and especially their prospects and their pursuits and occupations in life. He was always ready with advice and counsel when they were wanted. But he did not intrude them unduly, and above all things he did not insist upon their acceptance, or urge that his opinion and maxims should be made the rule of procedure. How admirably characteristic is his saying that 'he hoped none of his sons would ever believe anything because he said it, unless they were themselves convinced of its truth.'[63]

It is, it seems to me, merely delightful to feel that through all this interest and affection Darwin was constantly using his children, as he used himself, and everybody else, as material for the abstract scientific observation which was the main interest of his life. 'My first child was born on December 27th, 1839,' he tells us, 'and I at once commenced to make notes on the first dawn of the various expressions which he exhibited.'[64] How many fathers would have done as much? And the constant, watchful observation was continued at all times.

But it did not in the least interfere with the abundant, overflowing, sympathetic affection. And the affection was not distant, of the sort which adores but cannot enter in. His son indeed points out that health prevented his father's romping with the children or taking part in any rough play. But he shared their games, so far as he could, with eager interest and keen enjoyment, and made them feel that he was one of themselves and as themselves. When they all went off on a holiday, he entered into it with a youthfulness of enthusiasm which intensified the enthusiasm of everybody. He liked to have the children about, even if they interrupted his work, as they too frequently did; such a multitude of them in a house would be likely to. Especially when they were ill, his sympathetic care and watchfulness were soothing and comforting. His daughter quotes one of his cousins as a witness that 'in our house the only place where you might be sure of not meeting a child, was the nursery. Many a time, even during my father's working hours, was a sick child tucked up on his sofa, to be quiet, and safe, and soothed by his presence.'[65]

Dread of the children's illness and death at times haunted and oppressed him. Thus he writes to Hooker: 'To the day of my death I shall never forget all the sickening fear about the other children, after our poor little baby died.'[66] And the depth of his grief after losing his little daughter Annie appears quietly but profoundly in the letters written at that time.

As years passed, Darwin's relation to his children reached its climax of comradeship in the constant assistance they gave him in his work. His daughter helped him clerically, and his sons, who had scientific interests of their own, participated actively and most profitably in his labors. Sometimes he made use of their keen wits to sharpen and clarify his: 'Two of my grown-up children who are acute reasoners have two or three times at intervals tried to prove me wrong; and when your letter came they had another try, but ended by coming back to my side.'[67] Whatever the nature of the assistance might be, Darwin was always profoundly grateful for it, and his children speak particularly of the simple, humble fashion in which his gratitude was expressed. It was a pleasure to help him in any way, because you were sure that the help would be used as you meant it and would be thoroughly appreciated.

And in general I do not know that the beauty of Darwin's relation to his children can be better expressed than in the words of his son, equally honorable to son and to father: 'I do not think his exaggerated sense of our good qualities, intellectual or moral, made us conceited, as might perhaps have been expected, but rather more humble and grateful to him. The reason being no doubt that the influence of his character, of his sincerity and greatness of nature, had a much deeper and more lasting effect than any small exaltation which his praises or admiration may have caused to our vanity.' [68]

IV

Though Darwin's social activity was necessarily restricted by his ill-health, his devotion to special friends was as sweet and notable as his devotion to his family. Indeed, friendship, the natural turning to sympathetic spirits, and clinging to them with constant loyalty, seems to have been a peculiarly profound and powerful instinct in him. He took a deep interest in all his friends' affairs, and poured out all his own interests to them with intimate and appealing effusiveness. In writing of his grandfather, he says: 'There is, perhaps, no safer test of a man's real character than that of his long continued friendship with good and able men.'[69] Assuredly, if the test is applied to himself, he bears it nobly.

Of his longing for friendship and great aptness for it in boyhood he speaks very positively: 'I had many friends amongst the schoolboys, whom I loved dearly, and I think that my disposition was then very affectionate.'[70] His son says that the friendships of mature life had not quite the zest and passion of those of youth; but the son adds with justice that no one who reads his father's letters can feel that his later affections were lacking in intensity or depth.[71]

There can be no doubt that Darwin's influence over his friends was very great, probably all the more so because he was so unassertive and disinclined to interfere or to dictate. Sir John Lubbock is said to have 'owed to the great Charles Darwin even a larger debt in the respect of character formation than in the encouragement and direction of his mental gifts.'[72] Darwin did not hesitate to advise urgently and warmly, where he felt that advice was needed. For example, he writes to Hooker about his health: 'Take warning by me, and do not work too hard. For God's sake, think of this.'[73] He did not hesitate to differ, or to question, or to argue, when he thought his friends were wrong, and he could set them right.

At the same time, owing to his humility and natural self-effacement, the chief impression one gets from the intimate personal correspondence is that of turning to friends for counsel, encouragement, and support. Not that he was not amply able and ready to stand on his own feet; but to develop his views and arguments to others seemed to clarify them and to give them added force and significance for himself: 'I will write no more, which is a great virtue in me; for it is to me a very great pleasure telling you everything I do.'[74] Honor, commendation, appreciation, when they came from the public, were all very well; but their value and their charm were doubled when they came from those one loved. Thus, he writes in regard to a letter of Hooker, congratulating him on the receipt of a medal: 'I then opened yours, and such is the effect of warmth, friendship, and kindness from one that is loved, that the very same fact, told as you told it, made me glow with pleasure till my very heart throbbed.'[75] I have already alluded to his expressions of gratitude and appreciation for all the support and assistance that his friends gave him; but the expression is so tender, and so constant, and so thoroughly characteristic, that it cannot be too much insisted upon.

Nor was Darwin's affection for his friends lacking in the practical side any more than in the sentimental. He was ready to give his time and his strength in their service, though time was so limited and strength so much needed and so essential. When utter prostration makes assistance impossible, he reproaches himself bitterly, and zealously offers to make up the defect. As when he writes to Hooker: 'I write now to say that I am uneasy in my conscience about hesitating to look over your proofs, but I was feeling miserably unwell and shattered when I wrote. I do not suppose I could be of hardly any use, but if I could, pray send me any proofs. I should be (and I fear I was) the most ungrateful man to hesitate to do anything for you after some fifteen or more years' help from you.'[76] Or, in slighter matters, the sacrifice is given a

humorous turn, as when Darwin visits his old friend
Sedgwick and allows himself to be put through the
sights of the Museum without protest though he
suffers for the effort for a long time afterwards: 'Is
it not humiliating to be thus killed by a man of
eighty-six, who evidently never dreamed that he
was killing me?'[77]

And if time and strength, so vital and in general
miserly hoarded, were not spared, it is easy to
imagine that money was not. Scientists are not
always wealthy, and their researches require
ample means for their prosecution. Scientists
wear themselves out in eager toil and then are too
often hard put to it for funds with which to recup-
erate. Darwin was always watchful, interested,
ready, generous, and best of all unobtrusive in
supplying these needs. If his closest friend and sup-
porter Huxley broke down, Darwin was quick to
head a subscription to make recovery possible. If
he heard that a fellow-worker in Germany, who
was accomplishing great results with small means,
was hampered and embarrassed for lack of books,
he writes at once: 'Forgive me, but why should you
not order through your brother Hermann, books,
etc., to the amount of £100, and I would send a
check to him as soon as I heard the exact amount?

This would be no inconvenience to me; on the contrary, it would be an honor and lasting pleasure to me to have aided you in your invaluable scientific work to this small and trifling extent.' [78]

But the merely material relation of support and assistance was a small affair compared to the profound affection which Darwin seemed peculiarly calculated to convey and inspire. The note of this affection sounds through all his correspondence and gives it a more winning quality than almost anything else. How deep and strong was his friends' regard for him is nicely indicated in the passage in which Huxley analyzes the bearing of it upon his work and success: 'I cannot agree with you, again, that the acceptance of Darwin's views was in any way influenced by the strong affection entertained for him by many of his friends. What the affection really did was to lead those of his friends who had seen good reason for his views to take much more trouble in his defense and support and to strike out much harder at his adversary than they would otherwise have done. This is pardonable, if not justifiable — that which you suggest would to my mind be neither.' [79]

As for Darwin's own feeling, I know nothing that brings it home more vividly, when one considers his zeal for his work and for success with it, than the passage in which he declares such success and everything else to be trash beside love: "Talk of fame, honor, pleasure, wealth, all are dirt compared with affection; and this is a doctrine which, I know, from your letter, that you will agree with from the bottom of your heart.'[80] After which I think we may conclude generally that few human beings have been more endowed than Charles Darwin with tenderness and sympathy for all created things.

CHAPTER VI

DARWIN: THE DESTROYER

I

In studying the influence of Darwin and Darwinism, it is well to begin by realizing clearly the crude orthodox religious conceptions which prevailed with the mass of mankind through the Middle Ages and well into the nineteenth century, as they prevail still in some form among large portions of the population in Europe and America. According to these conceptions the universe was created by an omnipotent, thoroughly anthropomorphic Deity. In that universe the terrestrial globe occupied a most important, if not a central and pivotal position. The globe was peopled by living beings, each created by the Deity in its particular form and kind, and all, like the whole existing universe, subordinated to man, who alone was endowed with a reasoning intellect and a moral nature. Thus gifted, he was an object of peculiar solicitude to his Creator, who interfered in every aspect of human fate, and whose favor could be secured and his wrath deprecated by prayer and by the conformity of human conduct to the divine decrees.

In other words, the earth was the primary object of the universe, and man was the primary object of the earth, and hence of the universe also.

The speculations of Copernicus and the consequent development in modern astronomy, showing that the earth was not the center of the universe at all, but merely an insignificant and utterly inconsequential speck in the vastness of stellar space, gave this orthodox view a shattering shock. If the earth was of no consequence, how could man's consequence be supreme? Theology, with its fortunate gift of agile adaptation, after first combating the new astronomy with all its zeal, finally worked out to a belated acceptance of what could not be resisted, and then ingeniously contrived, by huge effort of reasoning, to reconcile science with orthodox views and to restore man to his supremacy. But just when this had been happily and satisfactorily accomplished, along came Darwin, and shattered human distinction and superiority, and with them the ancient ideas of Deity, even more completely than Copernicus had done. It is no wonder that theology, exhausted by the earlier struggle, was at times inclined to balk and give up the contest.

What interests us first is Darwin's own attitude

toward the far-reaching consequences of his theory. In an earlier chapter we have considered his religious views, so far as they affected him personally. We are now concerned with the larger aspect of their effect upon mankind as a whole.

That he was conscious of possible effects from the start is evident. He had lived closely enough in contact with the orthodox attitude to appreciate the results of disturbing it, and the deeper results of disturbing the fundamental principles upon which it was based. Nevertheless, he does not appear to have felt, or at least to have been haunted by, the dread of a solitary and God-abandoned universe that afflicts some of us. He was sensitive to concrete fears: 'You will then get rest, and I do hope some lull in anxiety and fear. Nothing is so dreadful in this life as fear; it still sickens me when I cannot help remembering some of the many illnesses our children have endured.'[1] But his general mental attitude was so healthy and so practical that he was not too much troubled by remote apprehensions and dim spiritual possibilities. Thus he was inclined to take an optimistic view of the workings of natural selection. He believed that, on the whole, the sum of happiness exceeded that of misery for sentient beings,[2] and he felt that indefinite progress and advancement for man were perfectly compatible with the conclusions to which his scientific study led him. As he puts it in 'The Descent of Man': 'To believe that man was aboriginally civilized and then suffered utter degradation in so many regions, is to take a pitiably low view of human nature. It is apparently a truer and more cheerful view that progress has been much more general than retrogression; that man has risen, though by slow and interrupted steps, from a lowly condition to the highest standard as yet attained by him in knowledge, morals, and religion.'[3] With these undeniably optimistic leanings on Darwin's part in mind, it is amusing to read Lyell's remark, that 'he had frequently been asked if Darwin was not one of the most unhappy of men, it being suggested that his outrage upon public opinion should have filled him with remorse.'[4]

At the same time, Darwin was perfectly aware that his theories tended to shatter the orthodox view of man and his supremacy and even the orthodox God. The sheer, simple statement of the matter appears in one vivid phrase: 'What a book a devil's chaplain might write on the clumsy, wasteful, blundering, low, and horribly cruel works of nature!'[5] Especially Darwin knew well what fierce hostility he should evoke from those who had grown up in the orthodox belief, were wedded to it by all the force of habit and tradition, and were intellectually unqualified to adapt themselves to any other. Therefore, from the beginning, he proceeded with the greatest caution and moderation of statement. This arose partly from his sweetness of temper. He had no desire to wound or destroy, except as the truth might compel him to do so. One early critic speaks admirably of 'the magnanimous simplicity of character which in rising above all petty and personal feeling delivered a thought-reversing doctrine to mankind with as little disturbance as possible of the deeply rooted sentiments of the age.'[6]

It was this caution and considerateness that induced him to write such passages as the conclusion of the 'Origin' with its interesting introduction for later editions of the phrase 'by the Creator' in the last sentence.[7] And the caution did not result wholly from timidity or unwillingness to shock, but was also brought about by Darwin's natural reluctance to commit himself in regions where he did not feel at home, or to take one step beyond the properly scientific province which he had really made his own. As to ultimate questions he confessed himself to be in 'a muddle,'[8] and why should he interfere with the more definite creed of others?

On the other hand, where his conclusions were clear and well established, he meant to speak out, and let the truth prevail, without regard to the feelings of anybody. He wanted to sustain no cause, to push no argument for itself, he wanted facts and nothing else. And when he feels that he has yielded too much to popular prejudice and to the desire to conciliate it, his regret is decided and he determines to do so no more: 'I have long regretted that I truckled to public opinion, and used the Pentateuchal term of creation, by which I really meant "appeared" by some wholly unknown process. It is mere rubbish, thinking at present of the origin of life; one might as well think of the origin of matter.'[9]

As regards this world, in questions of morals, of conduct, and generally of the bearing of evolution on sociology, Darwin's own sturdy moral habit and self-poised temperament made him perhaps unduly optimistic. Temptation had little hold upon him. Why should it have more upon others, even unsustained by celestial guidance and control? In 'The Descent of Man' he endeavors to show the social instinct as a sufficient and satisfactory basis

future of this earth: 'I quite agree how humiliating the slow progress of man is, but every one has his own pet horror, and this slow progress ... sinks in my mind into insignificance compared with the idea or rather I presume certainty of the sun some day cooling and we all freezing. To think of the progress of millions of years with every continent swarming with good and enlightened men, all ending in this, and with probably no fresh start until this our planetary system has been again converted into red-hot gas.' [15]

Yet when the question of the future has been debated over and over, the result, as with other questions, is complete muddle and puzzle, and all that can be said of them is: 'The conclusion that I always come to after thinking of such questions is that they are beyond the human intellect; and the less one thinks on them, the better.' [16] What at least stands out, is that Darwin does not greatly concern himself with the enormous dislocation of life in this world which is likely to follow the loss of belief in another.

And again, there is evolution and God. Darwin frequently insists that he is no atheist, and that his system must not be charged with any atheistical conclusion: 'Let each man hope and believe what he can. Certainly I agree with you that my views are not at all necessarily atheistical.'[17] The belief in God is eminently useful: 'With the more civilized races, the conviction of the existence of an all-seeing Deity has had a potent influence on the advance of morality.'[18] At every convenient opportunity God is given fair play and a fighting chance: it rests with Him to make the most of it. At the same time, the obstacles and difficulties are mountainous and it would appear insuperable. Thus, there is the conclusion of 'Plants and Animals Under Domestication': 'If we assume that each particular variation was from the beginning of all time preordained, then that plasticity of organization, which leads to many injurious deviations of structure, as well as the redundant power of reproduction which inevitably leads to a struggle for existence, and, as a consequence, to the natural selection or survival of the fittest, must appear to us superfluous laws of nature. On the other hand, an omnipotent and omniscient Creator ordains everything and foresees everything. Thus we are brought face to face with a difficulty as insoluble as is that of free will and predestination.'[19]

But the result in any case, if God is left in His universe at all, is to remove Him very, very far away, and completely to demolish all sense of His intervention in the little daily actions and experiences of common life and all intimate communion and conference with Him in regard to those actions. When 'The Descent of Man' is published, Mrs. Darwin writes to her daughter, quite simply: 'I think it will be very interesting, but that I shall dislike it very much as again putting God further off.'[20] For others besides Mrs. Darwin it reduced Him quite to the vanishing point.

But if Darwin himself was contented to let God alone, so far as possible, the more ardent and zealous of Darwin's followers were inclined to hustle the Creator out of the universe altogether. This was especially true of the aggressive Darwinians in Germany. They extended the deductions of evolution to all the practical workings of human life in a fashion which Darwin distinctly disapproved: 'What a foolish idea seems to prevail in Germany,' he writes, 'on the connection between Socialism and Evolution through Natural Selection.'[21] To Darwin's energetic disciple, Weisman, the evolutionary theory seemed as solidly established as that of gravitation: 'We know just as surely as that the earth goes round the sun, that the living world upon our earth was not created all at once and in

the state in which we know it, but that it has gradually evolved through what, to our human estimate, seem enormously long periods of time.'[22]
And in Weisman's opinion, evolution would go on
creating adequate moral ideals, as it has done in the
past: 'The number of those who act in accordance
with the ideals of purer, higher humanity, in whom
the care for others and for the whole will limit care
for self, will, it is my belief, increase with time and
lead to higher ethical conceptions, as it has already
done within the period of human existence known to
us.'[23] Häckel substituted an exuberant, triumphant
materialistic atheism for the crawling supersti-
tions of an earlier day.

In England Huxley endeavored to emphasize the
complete separation of religion and science, though
no one really knew better than he how fatally they
interlock at every step. Spencer, in providing
evolution with a metaphysical apparatus, extended
its bearing into all the regions of speculative
thought. It is not probable that he is much read at
present, but his 'First Principles' spread a wide
leaven of agnosticism among the youth of a generation ago, and I do not know where you will find
a more desolating statement of the possible bar-
renness of evolutionary results than in the con-

clusion of his Autobiography: 'Then behind these
mysteries lies the all-embracing mystery — whence
this universal transformation which has gone on
unceasingly throughout a past eternity and will go
on unceasingly throughout a future eternity? And
along with this rises the paralyzing thought —
what if, of all this that is thus incomprehensible to
us, there exists no comprehension anywhere? No
wonder that men take refuge in authoritative
dogma. . . . Lastly come the insoluble questions
concerning our own fate: the evidence seeming so
strong that the relations of mind and nervous
structure are such that cessation of the one accom-
panies dissolution of the other, while simultan-
eously comes the thought, so strange and so difficult
to realize, that with death there lapses both the
consciousness of existence and the consciousness of
having existed.'[24]

II

After considering Darwin's view of the practical
working of his discovery, it is interesting to sum up,
so far as is possible in such vague and indefinite
matters, one's own impression of the effect of the
popular acceptance of that discovery. And here I
must emphasize that I am not dealing with phil-

osophical or scientific theories, least of all with any such theories of my own, but am simply trying to suggest what seem to me the indirect and secondary workings of scientific theory in the minds of vast masses of people, even of those conventionally connected with the churches of various denominations. It is hardly necessary to say that Darwin's own teaching cannot be held directly responsible for those workings, and that many of them he would have completely rejected. Moreover, it must also be recognized that Darwin in large measure summarized and embodied the general scientific drift of the age. Especially we must not overlook the immense influence of practical as well as theoretical science in affecting contemporary life. An excellent editorial in the Saturday Review of Literature (May 8, 1926) emphasizes the importance of scientific invention and machinery on nineteenth- and twentieth-century living, and this importance, both direct and indirect, is almost incalculable. For example, printing has spread thought among the masses. The sewing-machine has changed the world of woman. The extraordinary development of transportation has enormously increased the superficial bustle and distraction of life, to the serious detriment of meditative and spiritual interests. Nevertheless, the evolutionary theory may be regarded as typifying and formulating all these complicated tendencies more fully and effectively than any other. How the theory has worked is well suggested in the pregnant words of Professor Osborn, though he is careful to insist that it is the misunderstanding, not the understanding, of evolutionary doctrine, that has caused the evil: 'It may be said without scientific or religious prejudice that the world-wide loss of the older religious and Biblical foundation of morals has been one of the chief causes of human decadence in conduct, in literature, and in art. This, however, is partly due to a complete misunderstanding of creative evolution, which is a process of ascent, not of descent.'[25]

Let us attempt to follow the workings of evolution in various phases of life and thought. Take, first, politics. We cannot perhaps establish two strongly opposed points of view in regard to the phenomena of political life better than by contrasted quotations. President Coolidge, speaking on October 29, 1926, said: 'I do not know any adequate support for our form of government except that which comes from religion.'[26] Professor Keller, writing of 'Societal Evolution,' says: 'What moves men . . .

is not thought, but emotion. And what sets emotion going is interest. . . . What sets the revolutions in motion, with the result of drastic selection in the codes, is not the cerebration of any one over great issues, but the unendurable discomfort and awakened emotions of the masses. Their interests have been so outraged that anything seems likely to be better than the present.'[27]

The great democratic movement of the past hundred and fifty years naturally far antedated Darwinism. Its roots were laid in the eighteenth century, with the teachings of the French philosophers, chiefly Rousseau, and the practical action of the American and French Revolutions. But the views of evolutionary science fitted admirably with the intense individualism of democracy, its proclamation of the right of the individual man to assert himself against every and all others, high or low, rich or poor.

After democracy has made its way in the world, it is interesting to see the effort of theology to claim it and to urge that the value and importance of the individual is a gradual effect and an essential element of Christian doctrine. It is true that Christianity has always proclaimed the equality of all souls before God and their equal need of salvation.

223

But it is equally true that the Church has always got along comfortably with every sort of tyranny and for centuries solemnly sponsored the divine right of kings, alleging at all times the unfailing text, 'Render unto Cæsar the things which are Cæsar's.' And it is more deeply true that the natural Christian emphasis upon the importance of another world tends to create indifference to the political concerns of this, so that, even in the middle of the nineteenth century, revivalists like Moody could regard political movements and reforms as matters of minor consequence in face of the imminent cataclysm which would wipe out this world and its doings altogether. The most vigorous and energetic insistance on the rights of man as a mortal came from those who concerned themselves very little with his immortality.

And if indifference to the other world affected politics, it has had an even greater effect in the more general regions of sociology. So long as the poor and wretched were taught — by the rich — that their sojourn here was infinitesimally insignificant compared with the bliss that awaited them hereafter, they could endure with comparative patience. Lazarus could let the dogs lick his sores with fair content, while he was comforted with the reflection that an equally bad day was coming for Dives, and a great deal more of it. But when he became convinced that this world was all, Lazarus bestirred himself, and invented Socialism and Anarchism and Bolshevism and many other isms with capital letters, which might enable him to attend to the matter of Dives right here and to see to it that, if he himself could not share all the blessings of the rich, at least the rich might be made as miserable as he. We have become so gradually accustomed to an adjustment to the standpoint of this world that we hardly realize how completely and vastly it has entered into the views and opinions of even those who do not explicitly admit it.

Take again the influence of science in the realm of art. From the close of the eighteenth century external nature began to play a rôle in the arts that it had never played before and the prominence of landscape in painting was as notable as natural description in literature. But during the first half of the nineteenth century this natural influence was romantic, imaginative, emotional. With the middle years the scientific tendency made itself felt, and art became more closely and intensely realistic. This is perhaps most generally obvious in the literary world, and the great novel-

ists of France from Balzac on embody the scientific
movement of which Darwin is so eminently representative. Most significant of all in this regard is
the great epic of Zola, the history of the Rougon-
Macquart family, in twenty solid volumes. I am
not for a moment vouching for the solidity of Zola's
science, which may be quite as fantastic in its way
as the romance of Dumas. The point is that Zola
believed himself to be typifying and illustrating
scientific tendencies, and that the popularly accepted notion of the struggle for existence, with all
its blind and bitter cruelty, its pitiful tragedy of
the warfare and merciless destruction of the animal
world, was transferred to humanity in the endless
pages, as gloomy as they are powerful, of the great
French imaginative drama. And it is interesting,
as we come right down to the present day, to find
a thoughtful critic attributing the ugly and realistic
tendencies of current American fiction not to any
passing upheaval caused by the World-War, but to
just this gradual influence of scientific thought
making itself felt everywhere: 'What we are looking
at is not the product of a decade or an episode, even
so supreme an episode as battle, but the fructifying
of scientific doctrines that for several decades have
been seeping into society. What we are witnessing

is the yielding of the romantic view of life to the scientific.' [28]

Thus scientific conceptions, working in the popular mind, have fixed it upon the affairs of this world, and have reduced the various phases of the other, formerly so immensely important, to a shadowy inconsistency. Science, for example, has disposed of hell with ludicrous completeness. The old material hell, as Dante and the Middle Ages viewed it, a repository definitely under ground, with devils busily engaged over boiling cauldrons, has surely vanished, never to return. In the scientifically arranged physical universe there is no place for it. Even my friend Moody, whose ideas of heaven were so specific, does not attempt any such physical location of hell. And it is true that the orthodox still take refuge in moral torments, prolonged if not eternal horrors, which the erring spirit in wilful perversity inflicts upon itself. But it is doubtful if even the orthodox continue to take even these very seriously. There cannot be many persons who still suffer from the brooding gloom with which the concrete vision of hell genuinely oppressed thousands of sensitive souls in ages past. And in some respects this may be set down as a gain, since the misery to the sensitive souls was

very real, while how far the fear of hell acted as a
deterrent to souls of another order is always open
to question. But, gain or loss, it will hardly be disputed that the boiling depths of hell have largely
boiled away.

Unfortunately hell, in departing, has shown a
marked tendency to drag heaven with it. The same
material difficulty of course obtains here also.
Moody used to proclaim that heaven was tangible,
mapable, a city like New York, only with more
agreeable streets and doubtless better traffic arrangements. But it is hard for the most devout believer to-day to take so concrete a view. And it is
not only that the pearly gates and golden pave-
ments have gone. Their disappearance has given
a rude jar to the belief in any kind of future
life whatever. I am merely speaking of the average American man in the street, and perhaps of
even the woman also. The negative views in such
matters announced shortly before his death by so
good, so upright, so in the largest sense Christian
a man as Luther Burbank, are beyond a doubt the
views more or less definitely formulated of millions
of men in America to-day. The best they can say
is, that it is their business to live the life here in
the most energetic, straightforward, profitable way

they can, to see that after their deaths their wives and children are provided for, and to leave any other lives to take care of themselves.

And then there is the question of God, and it seems that He has a tendency to vanish also, with the disappearance of His celestial habitation, so that I feel a pathetic touch of tenderness for departed grandeur in capitalizing the pronoun. The scientific sequence of cause and effect has permeated so thoroughly the minds of even those who do not think of it in formal terms that the old feeling of the intervention of Divine Providence in daily affairs and the old intimate relation with a personal Father have been greatly weakened where they have not been altogether forgotten. As Mrs. Darwin suggests, God grows further and further away. It is sometimes urged that this remoteness is connected with a deeper and more serious reverence, that our relation to the immanent Deity has become more worthily and profoundly spiritual; but there is great danger of revering Him out of existence. In the Middle Ages men treated God as familiarly as if He were a friend round the corner, but they felt Him.

Worship, at any rate Protestant worship, tends to lose its devotional character and the overpowering sense of the Divine presence, and to become a mere polite fraternizing for social purposes. You hear many people say that they worship God better alone in the fields than in the churches. As to some of the churches the feeling is natural enough, but I wonder how many think of Him on the golf-links, except in the form of profanity, or in the hurry and swirl of traffic-crowded highways, or even in the fields, if anybody ever gets there any more. And prayer? I have spoken in connection with Darwin of my old friend who prayed, though he had nothing to pray to. It may be that more keep up the habit than we suppose. But with how many is it still a passionate intercession for divine help in their daily needs or a means of self-forgetful communion with the comforting, supporting, everlasting Arms? How many boys still pray to have fence-rails lifted off them or to win in their games of baseball and football? Can we possibly conceive such a state of things as is indicated in Finney's description of a revival a hundred years ago? 'Indeed the town was full of prayer. Go where you would, you heard the voice of prayer. Pass along the street and if two or three Christians happened to be together, they were praying. Wherever they met, they prayed.'[29]

THE DESTROYER

The most striking of all the dislocations effected by the intrusion of the scientific attitude is in the banishment of sin. Not only original sin has been swept away with the disappearance of the older theology and the establishment of evolutionary doctrines, but the uneasy, haunting torment of conscience and remorse appears to have been greatly diminished. No doubt it still, as always, chiefly harasses those who have least need of it. No doubt some persons still vex themselves to agony for imaginary sins. But vast numbers, especially of the younger generation, are like the heroine of Lemâitre's play, 'a little woman who without any very definite idea of the meaning of positivism, Darwinism, struggle for life, etc., lives in a moral atmosphere impregnated with all these things.'[30] And as a consequence, her moral attitude undergoes the great transformation of the modern world, by which an old-fashioned sin becomes simply a new-fashioned mistake. In other words, expediency, the belief that it does not pay to do wrong, takes the place of the old divine sanction, divine command, divine reward and punishment.

There are many who take a very sanguine view of all this. To them it seems that the old, instinctive sense of sin was stupid and caused far more

misery than it cured. Expediency, or enlightened
self-interest, working with the larger interest of the
community, is expected more and more effectively
and satisfactorily to take the place of the older
categorical imperative. But to others it seems that
expediency is but a chill and slender reed to lean
upon when the stress of passion and temptation
comes. 'Oaths,' says Shakespeare, 'are straw to
the fire i' the blood.' The dread of hell was often
a mild deterrent enough, but it is doubtful whether
remote considerations of expediency will suffice to
deter even so effectively as hell-fire.

To these old-fashioned and conservative persons
it seems likely that the decay of a divine origin
will weaken and break down the springs of moral
action and that in an enlightened self-interest the
enlightenment is hardly powerful enough to abolish
the selfishness. Some of these persons have even
been disposed to see in the World War something at
least of the culmination of evolutionary doctrines
about the struggle for life and survival of the fittest,
and it is certainly in the protest against these
doctrines that the Fundamentalists find their best
justification for attempting to set back and repress
the movement of human thought, if there were
any justification whatever for the unwisdom of

an effort to dam the Mississippi with a sheet of paper.

III

When we turn from the popular acceptance of evolution and its workings, we may, if we choose, find plenty of interpretations of the theorists yielding a different result.

Long before Darwin's day evolution, in the sense of a larger process of development and unfolding in the universe, had been foreshadowed and cherished by the philosophers. Not to speak of the Greeks, the successors of Kant in Germany had, each in his way, devised some dynamic explanation of the spiritual world. Fichte had built his mystical metaphysic of the ego, Schelling had worked out his scheme of the adjustment of the I and the Not-I, Hegel had erected his superb logical edifice on the framework of thesis, antithesis, and synthesis, starting with the elements of being and non-being reconciled in the progressive thesis of becoming, which in itself seems to have the germ of the whole evolutionary development. Schopenhauer and Hartmann had followed somewhat similar lines in their pessimistic treatment of the Will and the Unconscious. So again, the thinking

of our own Emerson not only anticipates Darwin
in such detail as the lines I have already quoted,

'And striving to be man, the worm
Mounts through all the spires of form,'

but is eminently suggestive of evolution in the intensely dynamic, developmental quality of his
thought, which perhaps also, in its suggestion of a
Pantheistic indifference to immortality, may be
said to be as destructive to humbler human hopes
as Darwin was.

Also, there are the philosophers who, obviously
coming within the scope of evolution and Darwinism, transform and transfigure them with a certain
divine radiance and spiritual change. There is William James. Forty years ago I happened to ride in a
horse-car opposite James, who was talking with all
his splendid, eager enthusiasm to a pupil sitting beside him. James said that for a time he had been
oppressed by the gloom of Schopenhauer's pessimism. Then he had pulled himself together and
made up his mind that the true course for him was
to get rid of all the evil within his own reach, so far
as he personally could, and let the broader working
of the universe take care of itself. Here we see the
germ which later grew into the splendid fabric of
Pragmatism, the belief that the Spirit, which made

the world of evolving phenomena, was itself a thing of dynamic growth and force, able to create by its own native energy a future and a reality and a God that should embody its highest ideals. A parallel development appears in the 'Creative Evolution' of Bergson, the theory of the creative spirit perpetually evolving in richer, more splendid, more satisfying forms, through the eternal depths of a luminous future. From the day when Darwin's views were first announced up to this very moment, up to the publication of such books as Professor Whitehead's 'Science and Modern Thought' and Professor Lloyd Morgan's 'Emergent Evolution,' thinkers have been busily at work devising interpretations and developments of the evolutionary doctrine, regardless of conflict and divergence, in the spirit of Professor Whitehead's admirable saying, 'A clash of doctrines is not a disaster — it is an opportunity.' The results are somewhat bewildering, and perhaps rarely satisfying to any but the thinkers themselves, but they are at least stimulating and suggestive.

And there are the achievements of the clergy. As I have earlier pointed out, it took many generations of herculean effort to get the Bible and the Copernican theory into harmony, but by endless

processes of the reasonable wriggling which so
much amused Darwin in himself and others[31] the
two were contentedly brought together. Then appeared this later disturber of the peace, and at first
the theologians despaired. But when did a theolo-
gian ever quite despair? Mankind must have God,
must have Christ, must have the Bible, and above
all things must have a priesthood. If Darwinism
did away with the first three, I ask you what would
the priesthood do for a living? Therefore the contending elements must be reconciled, and should
be. Science in contradiction with religion? Fie!
Never! Why, science only clarifies religion, and
religion enriches and fructifies science. The marriage of the two is triumphantly proclaimed in the
joyous cry of Dr. Cadman, which typifies thousands of others, and demonstrates that everything
is for the best in the best of all possible clerical
worlds: 'So far from evolution being incompatible
with religion, it is of all scientific theories the most
easily accommodated to the demands of faith. In
itself the evolutionary hypothesis supplies to all
scientists and believers in religion one of the noblest
conceptions of the creative mind to be found anywhere in literature. The idea of progressive development culminating in perfectibility contains

the most radiant optimism extant to-day.'[32] It
would be difficult to improve upon the splendor of
that passage, but it offers vast food for meditation.
Somehow I turn from it instinctively to the comment of Darwin upon one of his orthodox admirers:
'How funny men's minds are! He says he is chiefly
converted because my books make the Birth of
Christ, Redemption by Grace, etc., plain to him!'[33]
How funny men's minds are!

And then there come along those pestilent Fundamentalists, with whom some of us are much inclined to sympathize, and declare that Darwinism
shatters the Bible and Christ altogether. But the
Bible, as they read it, is infallible. Therefore Darwinism must be wrong: let us crush it, and grind it,
and stamp it out of the world.

The optimism of the scientists is quite as persistent and perhaps a little more convincing than
that of the theologians. There are first those whom,
without meaning any slur, one may call the pseudo-
scientists, writers who have had no special scientific training or experience or discipline, but who
apply their quick literary wit to the consideration
of evolutionary problems as of many others. If
Messrs. Butler and Shaw and Wells and the rest
cannot be said to have made scientific contributions

of very great value, they have at least applied thoughtful, acute, suggestive analysis and stimulating conjecture in both religious and sociological lines.

The optimism of trained and professed scientists is, however, somewhat more serious and more important. From the advent of Darwin's theory there have been those, like Asa Gray, who persisted in regarding it as perfectly, luminously compatible with entire orthodoxy. Gray himself maintained this position with militant energy, and Mivart, though far more critical of Darwin, contrived to reconcile the general principles of evolution with a long adherence to the Catholic Church. In our day Sir Oliver Lodge has reconciled a life of scientific research with spiritualistic beliefs, and even Darwin's co-discoverer. Wallace, ardently advocated spiritualism to the end.

Others who are not quite so extreme in their conclusions, yet insist that there is no conflict whatever between a firm belief in Darwinism and a spiritual hope. Especially scientists of this type lay stress upon the benefits which enlightened scientific theory confers upon our life in this world. Evolution, according to them, teaches the splendid progress of man in the past and in the future, his enriching development, his enlarging solidarity in well-being and well-doing. When one reads these almost ecstatic interpretations of scientific possibility, one finds it really difficult to resist their rapture. Listen to the enthusiasm of Professor Conklin: 'The past and present tendencies of evolution justify the highest hopes for the future and inspire faith in the final culmination of this great law in

> "One far-off divine event
> ˙Toward which the whole creation moves." '[34]

The religion of the future is to be no worse than that of the past: who knows but it may be infinitely better? 'In the past religion has dealt to a large extent with the individual and his relation to God; its chief concern was the salvation of individual souls and their preparation for a future life; it has been largely *egocentric*. The religion of the future must more and more deal with the salvation of society; it must be *ethnocentric*.'[35] In the charming words of Meilhac and Halévy:

> 'C'est imprévu, mais c'est moral.
> Ainsi finit la comédie.'[36]

> 'Unexpectedly moral at that,
> It closes the comedy pat.'

To be sure, there are persons to whom all this ecstasy seems more gorgeous than substantial. I cannot help thinking of the bitter comment of Leopardi on the sciolists who were busily engaged in making a happy whole out of wretched component parts: 'The lofty spirits of my day found out a new and almost divine scheme: not being able to make any one person happy, they forgot individuals and set themselves to making the community happy as a whole.'[37] And he concludes,

'I know not whether to pity or to smile.'[38]

I confess that I am myself perfectly, enormously egocentric, and these *ethno* considerations appeal to me very little. In so far as the good of the race is identified with my personal comfort and well-being, I am interested in it. But my ego cries out for God simply for itself, and if it is to vanish like a dewdrop in the sun, words cannot express my utter indifference to the well-being of the race, of the world, and of the universe.

Nevertheless, it is probable that humanity will achieve some adjustment in this matter. Mankind has always demanded spiritual ideals and the divine presence, and always will demand them. If they are lost, it will re-invent them. If they are destroyed, it will re-create them. No doubt the speculations of the philosophers, the merry doings of the clergy, and the persistent optimism of the scientists will suffice to keep religion and the human soul and even God upon Their feet and to enable Them to carry on decorously through the dreamy flight of centuries to come.

IV

Meantime, it is interesting to consider how many of the great spirits of the last generation, and especially of those most intellectually influential, were profoundly moved by Darwinism and felt more or less its haunting gloom of destruction and its far-reaching effect. In Ibsen the struggle for existence shows itself in the intense assertion of the individual and his passionate emphasis of the right to live and develop himself, and the same tendency in Nietsche grew into the cloudy and colossal phantom of the Superman. With Tolstoi the obsession of Darwinistic conflict and survival appears in the earlier novels, 'Anna' and 'War and Peace,' but in the end, like Zola or John Fiske, he found the pressure too great and too horrible, and endeavored to establish an antidote for human misery in human love. In Renan the subtle, delicate, enchanting irony serves only to make the fundamental, dissolving nihilism more deep and ruinous. As he expressed it, through the dramatic characters who are merely his mouthpiece: 'Uncertain as we are about human destiny, the wisest course is to see to it that in making all sorts of hypotheses, one at least avoids being too absurd';[39] again: 'Though the universe should prove not serious, science might be serious still. Vast sums of virtue have been expended on chimæras. It is better to take the more virtuous course, even though one may not be sure that virtue is more than a word.'[40] Or our own American Henry Adams asks evolution to educate him, and asks in vain. All it can teach him is that *terebratula* can remain unchanged in its insignificance for centuries, while man evolves, yet in the end proves to be no whit more significant than *terebratula*. And Adams goes out, like a spent torch, uneducated, in the huge, unmeaning, whirling acceleration of theories and discoveries and plain sufferings and questions that must remain forever unanswered. Yet perhaps Adams was quite as adequate to the universe as Dr. Cadman.

There are, especially, two figures, not so important for the quality of their thought, but immensely important for the influence of it, who stand out as being overweighted and overcome by the evolutionary blight. Anatole France, following Renan, filled his books and his life with gentle, indulgent, kindly tolerance, with rare human insight and sympathy. Yet beneath it all, beneath the lenient tenderness of Sylvestre Bonnard, and the kindly curiosity of Jérôme Coignard, and the patient comprehension of Monsieur Bergeret, always there was the sense of the nullity of human effort and the futility of human fate. All the motives and interests of men and women are reduced to the Darwinian residuum of self-preservation and propagation, or as France repeatedly puts it, more boldly and baldly, love and hunger are the two poles of our being. And when he makes intimate confession of the workings of the theory in his own person and life, this is the result: 'It is said, "Man is the lord of creation." Man is the lord of suffering, my friend. There is no clearer proof of the non-existence of God than life. . . . If you could read in my soul, you would be terrified. . . . There is not in all the universe a creature more unhappy than I. People think me happy. I have never been happy for one day, not for a single hour.'[41]

Or take the case of Mark Twain, far more important for Americans than Anatole France, because it may safely be said that few if any authors more influenced and to-day influence the youth of America than the creator of Huckleberry Finn.

Mark, like France, was the kindest, the gentlest, the most humane of men and writers. His energetic sympathy and support were given to relieve suffering and oppression everywhere. But although he was not particularly expert in science or philosophy, the plague of utter nihilistic disbelief had infected his soul as completely as that of France, and far more militantly. The destructive effect of the evolutionary teaching cannot be more fully displayed than in the arguments which Mark, to save his own credit, puts into the mouth of Satan in 'The Mysterious Stranger': 'A God . . . who mouths justice and invented hell — mouths mercy and invented hell — mouths Golden Rules, and forgiveness multiplied by seventy times seven, and invented hell; who mouths morals to other people and has none himself; who frowns upon crimes, yet commits them all; who created man without invitation, then tries to shuffle the responsibility for man's acts upon man, instead of honorably placing it where it belongs, upon himself; and finally, with altogether divine obtuseness, invites this poor, abused slave to worship him!'[42]

In conclusion, perhaps one may introduce oneself, not in the least as connected with all these distinguished persons, but simply as a type of a great number of average human beings, who live and suffer and have to fight their way somehow through the blinding mist of years and tears. When I was sixteen, I read the 'Origin,' and I think the impression it produced has never been obliterated. It is not, it has never been, the maintenance of any deliberate philosophical theory. I am too utterly without intellectual training or equipment even to form such a thing. It is not any aggressive or militant agnosticism. It is simply a feeling of utter insignificance in face of the unapprehended processes of nature, such as Leopardi expresses with bare intensity: 'Nature in all her workings has other things to think of than our good or ill.' [43] It is a sense of being aimlessly adrift in the vast universe of consciousness, among an infinity of other atoms, all struggling desperately to assert their own existence at the expense of all the others.

Apparently this sense of struggle among individuals, struggle everywhere, among theories and beliefs, as well as living creatures, does not affect every one with the same oppression of distress. There are natures so healthily constituted that they have the mere joy of adventure in it, and can go on forever elbowing their way through the crowd of other nothings with the splendid affirmation of their individuality in the conflict. If it is a question of theories, they can say with Professor Whitehead: 'A clash of doctrines is not a disaster; it is an opportunity.' If it is a case of more material strife, they can disguise it with the ameliorations of the social instinct, or such substantial optimism as sustained President Eliot through his ninety years in the view that the joy of life is in 'contest without conflict.'

More infirm, more frail, more doubting tempers may not take it so. There is the weary horror of endless multiplicity, sweeping from eternity to eternity. There is the embodiment of the universe in one individual, and yet the sense that that individual is more fragile than the universe itself, the sense that reduces all life and all one is to a mere shifting maze and complication of fleeting sensations, held together by the vaguest gauze of memory, and liable to be scattered and disseminated at any moment by the slightest shock. No doubt the corrective for such a dissolving terror is to live intensely in one's own personality, without thinking of it, to emphasize every moment *instinctively* the huge importance of one's ego, which if it has its way is at all times adequate to fill the endless spaces of the universe and crowd out the major stars. But for some of us such emphasis is difficult to accomplish, and instead, when one is thoroughly penetrated by the evolutionary attitude, one is too apt to find oneself more insignificant than *terebratula*, because one is conscious of one's own insignificance and *terebratula* is not.

And it was Darwin, the gentle, the kindly, the human, who could not bear the sight of blood, who raged against the cruelty of vivisection and slavery, who detested suffering in men or animals, it was Darwin who at least typified the rigorous logic that wrecked the universe for me and for millions of others.

CHAPTER VII

DARWIN: THE SCIENTIFIC SPIRIT

I

INDEPENDENTLY of his actual scientific work and discoveries, Darwin is in so many respects one of the finest types of the scientific spirit, that it seems natural to conclude a study of him with a summary of the most important elements of that spirit, its admirable and broadly valuable qualities and its limitations, as illustrated in Darwin himself and in others as compared with him.

The basis and fundamental motive of the scientific spirit is simply and naturally curiosity, the endless and often merely wayward desire to know and to find out facts, of all sorts. When the mind begins to shake itself clear of the immediate, engrossing pressure of mere subsistence, its first impulse is to learn something about the surrounding universe and about itself. And this impulse is not solely for utility, for the immense practical advantage which such knowledge evidently brings with it. There is the instinct of occupation and distraction, the effort to escape ennui and idleness and to fill one's thoughts with outward diversity that they may not

CHARLES DARWIN
About 1854

be dragged and weighed down by one's own particular cares and troubles. There is the instinct of emulation, the desire to excel others in knowledge, if one cannot in wealth, or in success of practical achievement.

These are the motives of the collector, and in a sense the scientist is a collector of facts, as others collect coins, or stamps, or china, or old furniture. The impelling motives of curiosity and excellence are much the same. There are people who gather and assort clippings from the newspapers, for the mere collecting instinct of it, gather them on all sorts of subjects, with the scientist's obscure impulse to accumulate knowledge even if they do not use it.

We are too apt to associate science exclusively with the study of nature, and in this way the thought of the scientific spirit is altogether too much restricted. Its real field is as vast as that of human interests, and scientific methods and scientific purposes apply as much to philology, to history, to religion, to the general movements of human society, as to the curious consideration of animals and plants and stones and chemical elements.

But if mere curiosity is to become truly scientific, it must be broadened and deepened into research. That is, the simple collection of facts must be systematized by a definite object and method. The mere garnering of one fact and another here and there, though it often has its great and singular charm, is apt to degenerate into aimlessness and futility. It must be guided and solidified by the sense of working toward some particular conclusion which will give all the facts coherence and significance. In other words, the relation of the facts must be studied, as well as the facts themselves, they must be coördinated and subordinated, till their real depth of meaning is revealed. How nicely does Darwin indicate the proportionate connection between theory and observation in the following passage: '*Let theory guide your observations*, but till your reputation is well established, be sparing in publishing theory. It makes persons doubt your observations.'[1]

Two of the supreme elements of research are completeness and correctness. It is true that final completeness can rarely be obtained in this world, but the important thing is to aim at it, to leave no stone unturned, no nook unsearched, to gather every possible fact from every possible source, before one allows oneself to deduce positive conclusions, or conclusions that even approach positiveness. And besides the completeness, one should test one's position from every aspect, to insure its being, so far as possible, correct. No one but the trained scientific thinker appreciates thoroughly the vast possibility of error, or is sufficiently aware how apt error is to intrude its subtle and treacherous working into the most careful investigations and the most logically buttressed theories. In one of his immensely suggestive casual phrases Darwin remarks, 'The history of error is quite unimportant.'[2] This may be true enough as regards the abstract progress of science, but assuredly the history of error is of the highest interest to the curious student of the human mind.

. But neither curiosity nor even the ardor of research will go very far, unless backed up by a habit of enormous and persistent industry. It is not the showy spurts that count, the bursts of application for a few weeks or months. It is the long, assiduous unbroken labor, such as thousands of scientists are giving in hundreds of laboratories, without prospect of distinction, without hope of immediate reward, simply from pure love of the work itself. And this toil is expended not only on the practical inventions, which are expected to produce comparatively quick and often astonishing commercial

processes of nature must be accepted and awaited. If it takes years to develop the experiments that will, or that even may, lead to the desired results, then you must accept the years, unhurrying, unworrying, with the assurance that the work will be done in the end and that it makes no difference to the world or to the future, whether it is done by you or by another.

And with the patience goes caution, the determination not to state results until you have confirmed them, not to overstate or give them forms that are misleading. In practical life, the necessity of acting at once often makes caution a dangerous luxury, and those who hesitate and debate too long are apt to arrive too late or not at all. A certain amount of chance and hazard must be taken and accepted. But the beauty of these larger intellectual realms of scientific thought is that you can wait calmly till all doubt and error are eliminated. The lesson of moderation is hard to learn. The best and the most careful never feel that they have learned it thoroughly: 'The subject has begun to interest me to an extraordinary degree,' says Darwin; 'but I must try not to fall into my common error of being too speculative. But a drunkard might as well say he would drink a little and not too much.'[5] And elsewhere, after years had weighted his work with the teachings of experience, he sums up what seems to him one of the supreme needs of science, if not the supreme need: 'Forgive me for suggesting one caution; as Demosthenes said, "Action, action, action," was the soul of eloquence, so is caution almost the soul of science.'[6]

Also, when you are testing so widely and carefully, and making sure of your foothold before every step you take, you come to realize the vast possibilities of different points of view. The one thing that the true scientist dreads is fixity, positiveness. Nature is forever mobile and flexible, and those who would follow nature and study her and interpret her must welcome and imitate her flexibility. They must be at all times ready to recognize the different aspects and phases of the same fact or group of facts, and willing to accept different conclusions with the changing and shifting light in which the facts are viewed. As Professor Whitehead puts it, admirably: 'Science is even more changeable than theology. No man of science could subscribe without qualification to Galileo's beliefs, or to Newton's beliefs, or to all his own scientific beliefs of ten years ago.'[7] As I read in an

excellent article in a field of scientific research very
different from Darwin's, that of philology and the
emendation of classical texts: 'In emending these
passages we should adopt Pasteur's method of investigation — exhaust every combination which it
is possible for the mind of man to conceive.'[8]

This impartiality, this breadth of view, this
readiness to consider, if not to accept, all conjectures and all theories, is comparatively easy, when
one is indifferent. If the motive of one's investigation is mere curiosity, and one has no doctrine to
establish, no thesis to defend, open-mindedness is
facile and natural. But the scientific man instinctively forms theories, and when once a theory is
formed, there comes the human impulse to maintain it, and to consider only those arguments and
even those facts that will bear one out. As we have
seen, it is here almost more than anywhere that
Darwin's example is of abiding value. No man
could be more attached to a theory than he was to
his. Yet he was determined, so far as human nature is capable of it, to keep his mind open and not
to let his preconceptions color his observation or
his reasoning. Huxley's statement of the matter is
indisputably correct when he speaks of Darwin's
'sagacity, his untiring search after the knowledge of

fact, his readiness always to give up a preconceived opinion to that which was demonstrably true.'[9] And Darwin, in another of his simple, striking phrases, condenses all that open-mindedness means, and the difficulty of it and the rarity (italics mine): 'If you argue about the non-acceptance of Natural Selection, it seems to me a very striking fact that the Newtonian theory of gravitation, which seems to every one now so certain and plain, was rejected by a man so extraordinarily able as Leibnitz. *The truth will not penetrate a preoccupied mind.*'[10]

Finally, among these more impersonal elements of the scientific spirit, a high place should be accorded to the quality of being ready to admit one's ignorance. In this age of universal ignorance, most people who think are more or less aware of their deficiency, but as we are naturally more appreciative of our own lack than of that of others, the first impulse is a desperate effort to conceal it. Perhaps of all states of mind one of the most hostile to the scientific spirit and most incompatible with it, is pedantry, and one of the most essential elements of pedantry is precisely this disposition to conceal one's ignorance, to make the most determined attempt to hide from others the fact that we are as helpless and as groping and as uncertain as they are. This is apt to be the vice of the teaching profession, though so many teachers are gloriously exempt from it. The pedagogue is inclined to think, I believe quite wrongly, that if he once lets his scholars see that there is anything he does not know, they will lose confidence in him forever, whereas nothing establishes their confidence so much as to appreciate his willingness to enter into their difficulties and to admit that the difficulties are human and his own.

At any rate, the true man of science begins by admitting the vastness of the regions that he has not entered and can never enter, the illimitable fields of knowledge that he has not the time or the training to explore. And no man was ever more notable in this admission than Darwin. There is the general recognition of the limits of human knowledge and human capacity for knowledge: 'The more one thinks, the more one feels the hopeless immensity of man's ignorance.' [11] There is the recognition of the hardening of the mental arteries, so to speak, by which our flexibility is so greatly impaired and against which we cannot guard enough: 'nearly all men past a moderate age, either in actual years or in mind, are, I am fully convinced, incapable of looking at facts under a new point of view.' [12] Further, there is not only the sense of general intellectual impotence, but the admission that, even in one's own special line, there is much that one must necessarily miss, much that must, if not invalidate one's conclusions, at least render them dubious and incline one to the extremest modesty in asserting them. No doubt the peculiar nature of Darwin's work, which obliged him to touch upon all sorts of very different scientific fields, accentuated this modesty of attitude, but no one can question that it was inborn: 'There are so many valid and weighty arguments against my notions, that you, or any one, if you wish, on the other side, will easily persuade yourself that I am wholly in error, and no doubt I am in part in error, perhaps wholly so, though I cannot see the blindness of my ways.' [13] When one goes after the truth in that spirit, one is much more likely to find it, and at any rate to teach the world valuable lessons, whether one finds it or not.

II

Now to consider the more personal qualities of the scientific spirit, that is those that affect human relations. Naturally it is not pretended that all scientific men have these personal qualities, any more than the qualities already indicated. Men of science are human like the rest of us, and eminently liable to the weaknesses that the rest of us have. Sometimes even they seem more liable, perhaps because the impersonality of their occupation makes the personal weaknesses stand out. But such weaknesses are obviously not a result of the scientific spirit, but obtain in spite of it, and its higher tendency should be to diminish or restrain them.

It is interesting, in this personal and human connection, to see how the scientific qualities develop into virtues to some extent akin to the Christian ideal. For example, the recognition and admission of ignorance, on which we have been insisting, must carry with it, should carry with it, the eminently Christian virtue of humility. When you are oppressively aware how little you know, how far your information is from being adequate and your conclusions from being final, it is impossible to maintain a spirit of arrogance or self-assertion. You turn to others for their agreement and support, in the tone of Goethe's remark that he felt immensely strengthened in a conclusion if he found that even one other human being agreed with him. Or, as Darwin puts it: 'Though I, of course, believe in the truth of my own doctrine, I suspect that no belief is vivid until shared by others.' [14] The truly scientific worker should be ready to defer to the opinion of his fellow-workers and instantly to surrender his own when convinced that theirs is based upon wider observation or more valid arguments.

Closely connected with humility is tolerance, and this virtue also flows from the admission of ignorance almost as a necessity. If you appreciate your limitations and that your knowledge is as incomplete as your deductions are hazardous, you will be at all times ready to recognize that others may be right and you may be wrong, and you will have a gentle forbearance toward even what appear to be their errors. 'True science necessarily carries tolerance with it,' says Voltaire. [15]

To be sure, the mention of Voltaire in connection with tolerance rather makes one smile, for if he fought for tolerance as for other things, he fought hard and bitterly, and he was always fighting for something. And in general it may well be urged that the history of scientific thought shows anything but tolerance and gentleness. Indeed it sometimes seems as if scientists were a peculiarly waspish and petulant generation, apt to fly out, and to fly at, with what to the ordinary mind hardly encourage this disposition to enter into the lives of others, because by its abstract character and its larger aims and interests it inclines to reduce as much as possible the elements of self, and of self-interest and self-assertion. Indeed, here again it is curious to see how, when the pursuit of scientific truth rises to its highest intensity and white heat of ardor, it brings about a sort of self-abnegation, which approaches and suggests the mystical self-abandonment of Christian ecstasy. He shall leave all and follow me, says religion. And we have seen something of the same spirit in Darwin's apparently colder declaration that the man of science should have neither wife nor child, but a heart of stone, and a brain altogether free for the vast, abstract researches which make the whole of his life.

There is indeed something almost religious in the passion with which the true scientist casts aside all personal considerations, often all considerations of comfort and ease and indolent enjoyment, in the absorbing effort to attain the pure truth which he is seeking. With what intensity of delight does one fling an old delusion behind him. As Darwin puts it: 'To kill an error is as good a service as, and sometimes even better than, the establishing of a new truth or fact.' [19] With what rapture does one become aware of the progress of scientific thought: 'How grand is the onward rush of science; it is enough to console us for the many errors which we have committed, and for our efforts being overlaid and forgotten in the mass of new facts and new views which are daily turning up.' [20]

It is needless to say that thousands of others besides Darwin are infected with this rapture, and to quite the same or an even greater degree. In the dawn of scientific thought we have Lucretius, than whom none was ever more ardent, exulting in his passionate effort to dart the beams of intellectual day through the swirling, smothering mist of error and delusion. Or again, in our own time we have such excitement as is described by Pasteur, so nearly the correlative of Darwin in many ways, when he feels himself to be on the brink of discovery: 'I was so happy that I was overcome by a nervous trembling that made it impossible for me to bring my vision again to the polarizing apparatus.' [21]

So the pursuit of pure truth, and the giving one's life to the achievement of it, elevates, and clarifies, and chastens, almost like the pursuit of virtue, and the two tend even to merge in one another, as in Goethe's noble saying: 'The real love of truth cation of the scientific spirit with the more personal elements. Sainte-Beuve made much more definite assertion than Darwin did, of sacrificing and effacing the personal life for scientific purposes. The Frenchman boasted that he mingled with all sorts of groups and associated himself with all sorts of causes and experiences, not from devotion to the things themselves, but from pure curiosity and from the passion for analyzing the working of these causes in human minds. He carried this so far that he was often accused of disloyalty to his friends, and of espousing causes and then deserting them, and he himself handles the defense of the subjective attitude in such a way as to give some justification for the charge. His life, his thought, his work, were perfectly impersonal, he said, and in consequence he was epigrammatically branded with betraying all truths for the sake of truth.

On the other hand, it is very evident that some personal elements lingered about him much more than he thought or admitted. His early ambition, his undying ambition, was to be a poet. As a poet he failed, at least made no popular or conspicuous success. He saw the ardent contemporaries and close associates of his youth, Hugo, Lamartine, Balzac, Sand, Musset, making great popular reputations, while he was compelled to drag along in comparative shadow; and for all his boasted impersonality, this to a certain extent embittered him. The vast comprehension, the high intellectual impartiality, which distinguish him when he is dealing with the past, fail and shrink in a measure when he discusses contemporary work, and you cannot but feel that he is unconsciously hampered and tormented by a jealousy from which Darwin was wholly and nobly free.

But what marks Sainte-Beuve's work most of all, as I have elsewhere emphasized, and what distinguishes him from Darwin and many other notable scientists, is the extraordinary concreteness of it. He had of course a vast background of general intellectual training and experience and of conversance with general thought and principles. But with this background always instinctively present, he devoted himself directly to the study of individuals. Only rarely does he deal in the discussion of theories of any sort, and then his handling is apt to be so complex and difficult that you feel him to be out of his element. What fascinates and absorbs him is the endless, close, minute, sympathetic study of individual men and women, and just because he is not hampered by theories, has no ends to attain nor points to prove, the study is endlessly varied, flexible, mobile, adaptable, and profoundly, inexhaustibly human. The incessant, fruitful application of scientific method has never been better exemplified than in Sainte-Beuve's work.

Or, to take another of the broader types of the scientific spirit, perhaps one of the noblest and most luminous that has ever existed, Goethe. Goethe was a half century older than Sainte-Beuve and Darwin, but he lived well down into their period and the clarity of nineteenth century scientific thinking could find no better example than he. His actual scientific work is far from contemptible, and he to some extent anticipated Darwin as to the possibilities of metamorphosis in the natural world. His speculations on the theory of light, in contradiction to those of Newton, show at least the active and energetic intelligence.

But Goethe's value to the scientific spirit rests on far broader grounds than any mere detail of scientific research or experiment. No one cultivated or practiced more than he the attitude of vast, unprejudiced curiosity, of eager search and relish for pure truth, independent of all considerations of party, or consequence, or practical bearing. It is this spiritual latitude which Matthew Arnold means when he calls Goethe the greatest poet of his own time and the greatest critic of all times. The free, broad, ample, mobile working of the human intelligence has never found a more lucid exponent than Goethe, and everywhere through his writings there are passages which will help the lover of truth, while the distilled essence of his mental attitude is to be found in the collection of 'Maximen und Reflexionen,' which gives the kernel of wisdom without the somewhat otiose Teutonic wrapping of amplification in which Goethe was often inclined to envelop it.

It is in the highest degree curious, remembering the weaknesses of Sainte-Beuve to which I have already alluded, to read all his numerous comments on Goethe, but particularly the following: 'Goethe understood everything in the universe — everything except perhaps two things, the Christian and the hero. There was a weakness here which belonged to the realm of heart. It seems likely that he considered Leonidas and Pascal, the latter especially, as *monstrosities* in the order of nature.'[25] And Sainte-Beuve prided himself upon understanding the Christian and the hero both, and it is probable that he did.

The interesting point in Goethe, and also in less degree in Sainte-Beuve, as compared with Darwin, is that the full development of the scientific spirit in both of them did not exercise the same sort of spiritual blight with which Darwin thought that it affected him. No human being ever lived who was more susceptible to beauty than Goethe was, and his passion for pure truth did not prevent his retaining the highest sense of artistic ecstasy through his whole long life. With him and with Sainte-Beuve both, it could hardly be said that thinking came before emotion, for both of them adored the incomparable beauty of form and the rapture that came with it up to the very end.

On the other hand, neither Goethe nor Sainte-Beuve is for a moment to be compared with Darwin in that ineffable sweetness and simple charm which endeared him to all who came into contact with him and which breathe everywhere through his letters and even his more formal scientific works.

One striking feature in Sainte-Beuve is that he recognized fully the absorbing, engrossing nature of the scientific spirit, yet appreciated that the pursuit of knowledge does not necessarily bring happiness. No one has expressed the barren desolation of mortal life with more acrid bitterness than he. Shakespeare tells us that ripeness is all. Sainte-Beuve doubts whether it exists. 'Ripen?' he cries. 'Ripen? We never ripen. We harden in some spots. We rot in others. We ripen never.'[26] Years bring with them — for him — an utter indifference to everything and everybody: 'I have arrived in life at a complete indifference: provided I do something in the morning, and go somewhere at night, life has nothing more for me.'[27] And again, life is nothing but the pricking of one illusion after another, till one becomes bitterly convinced that no illusion is worth the pains of being pricked. As he sums it up in a vivid figure: 'Why I no longer care for nature, for the country? Why I no longer care to walk in the little footpath? I know well that the footpath is the same, but *there is no longer anything on the other side of the hedge.* In old times there was rarely anything, but always there might be something.'[28]

It is true that Sainte-Beuve's melancholy and disgust are closely connected, as he himself admits, with the gross sexual disorders of his celibate career, and he speaks of 'the incurable disgust with everything which is peculiar to those who have abused the sources of life.'[29] In his later years he seems to have had no principle of sexual restraint

whatever, and to have indulged as freely in indis-
criminate commercial amours as did Pepys or
Aaron Burr, though he was as much without Burr's
gay oblivion as without Pepys's touches of remorse.
He proclaims as a cynical creed his method of seeking wisdom: 'Like Solomon and like Epicurus, I
have made my way to philosophy through pleasure. It is a better road than traveling thitherward
by logic after Hegel's or Spinoza's fashion.'[30] And
the sum of the philosophy was akin to Solomon's.
'Sainte-Beuve said to me,' records Goncourt, 'One
should make the tour of everything and believe in
nothing. There is nothing real but woman.'[31]
Solomon would hardly have made the exception.
The curious thing is that, with all this abandoned
personal license, Sainte-Beuve, in his critical judg-
ments, preserved the most delicate sensibility as to
moral excellence in sexual lines, as in all others.

When we turn to Goethe, we find perhaps little
more regard for sexual morals than with Sainte-
Beuve, but at any rate a temperament far better
poised, and to all appearances charged and glorified
with luminous serenity. Yet with Goethe also the
scientific spirit, even though enriched with the
artist's delight and the artist's creative power,
could not bring happiness in its train. The sor-

rows and sufferings of Werther might perhaps be accredited to the extravagance of youth. But in extreme old age we hear Goethe proclaiming the emptiness and misery of life in terms almost as bitter and complete as those of Sainte-Beuve or of Anatole France. 'I will say nothing,' he said to Eckermann, 'against the course of my existence. But at bottom it has been nothing but pain and burden, and I can affirm that during the whole of my 75 years I have not had four weeks of genuine well-being. It is but the perpetual rolling of a rock that must be raised up again forever.' [32]

So far as we know, Darwin had no sexual cause of spiritual disturbance, and his scientific pursuits obviously brought him interest and delight. But we have seen how much even Darwin complained that absorption in science stunted and atrophied the higher sides of the spiritual nature. Work was largely a means of forgetting life, and when work failed, Down cemetery became singularly attractive. The pursuit of truth for itself, exciting and engrossing as it may be, would seem to have something abnormal and unwholesome about it and Pascal's consolation for the reedlike insignificance of man in the thought that he is a 'thinking reed' sounds a little chill and comfortless, even with

Scherer's amplification about the glory of 'the dream that knows itself to be a dream, of thought that thinks itself.' The final emptiness and futility which at times appear to attach to the profoundest search for truth have never been more grandly stated than in the words with which Sainte-Beuve brings his vast history of Port Royal to a close: 'I have been and I am only an investigator, a sincere observer, attentive and scrupulous. . . . I have been after my fashion a man of truth, so far as I have been able to attain it. But how little is the best we can attain! How bounded is our vision and how quickly it reaches its limit! It is like a pale torch lighted for a moment in the midst of an enormous night. And he who most had it at heart to know his subject, who had the keenest desire to grasp it, and the greatest pride in treating it, most feels himself impotent and below his task, on the day when, seeing it almost completed and the result obtained, the intoxication of power fails him, the final exhaustion and the inevitable disgust overwhelm him, and he perceives that he too is but an illusion the most fleeting on the breast of the Illusion which is infinite.' [33]

THE SCIENTIFIC SPIRIT

IV

And of course it is not contended that scientific men in general are unhappy, which would be absurd. On the contrary, it is probable that, with the infinite variety and solace of their pursuits, they are apt to be an unusually contented and cheerful class of men. There is the poignant saying of Voltaire, who was full of the scientific spirit as of most others: 'Study consoles for everything.'[34] And Montesquieu expresses it more generally: 'I have never had a sorrow which a half hour of reading would not dissipate,' and again, with more specific elaboration: 'The love of study is almost the sole passion that is eternal in us; all the others fail as this miserable machine which sustains them falls more and more into decay.'[35]

Yet for the mass of mankind assuredly the scientific spirit and the pure pursuit of truth are not enough, and the abstract thought of them leaves a void which only persistent, concentrated action can fill up. We are living, moving, acting creatures, and for most of us knowing, thinking, except as a means to living, is inadequate, infertile, and essentially provocative of discontent. As Sterne's Yorick expresses it, in his homely, pointed fashion: 'I think the procreation of children as

277

The extreme illustrations are in such minds as Sénancour, Maine de Biran, Amiel, men naturally equipped for the performance of great things, but in whom the force of genius is paralyzed by the perpetual introspective consideration of the means and methods by which genius operates. As Amiel expresses it: 'I also feel at times the mad rage for life, the desperate impulse to seize happiness, but much more often a complete prostration and a silent despair. And whence comes this? From doubt of my own reason, of myself, of men, of life, from doubt which enervates the will and destroys the powers, which makes one forget God, forget prayer, forget duty, from unquiet and corrosive doubt, which renders existence impossible, and makes a ghastly mock of hope.'[38]

Perhaps reason offers the most curious of all the antinomies or self-contradictions which arise when one seeks to develop the physical, mental, and moral nature of man, on an evolutionary basis, from the fundamental instinct of self-preservation. A lesser but striking form of this self-contradiction is, for example, the habit of thrift, which is naturally explained as a tendency of self-protection, yet in its sordid extremes may work to destroy life rather than prolong it. Or, again, there are the strange contradictions involved in the social instinct. As one sees it in the insects, or in the gregarious grouping of the lower animals, the self-preservational basis is obvious enough, and with a few wrenches of excusable ingenuity one may put all human affections and devotions on the same foundation. Yet in the end one arrives at the astonishing paradox that the instinct of self-preservation has developed devotion to others so that a man may be willing to lay down his life for his friend, or even for those who are not his friends. But the extreme of all these contradictions, if one accepts the evolutionary development of reason, is that that marvelous instrument should be produced for the preservation of the individual and yet that the final working of it should be to show how utterly insignificant, pitiable, and unworthy of preservation this very individual is.

Another weakness of the scientific spirit, and the curse of its passion for truth, is the difficulty, not to say the impossibility of ever attaining it. In the detail of scientific research this is, perhaps, not an evil, and difficulty is merely a splendid spur and stimulus to ever renewed effort and achievement. But when it comes to profounder and more fundamental matters, the difficulty is more serious, and may know, he may know, especially as he thinks he does, which goes so vastly far, but I, I, I, alas, do not.

Agnosticism is too violent a word for this purely personal and infinitely humble ignorance. Scepticism even is too proud a word, too philosophical a word. Yet scepticism, if used with caution, may perhaps serve, for want of a better. But there is one thing about scepticism too often forgotten. Universal doubt surely carries with it the privilege of universal hope. The professed sceptic is too apt to be critical and cynical, to use his doubt simply to upset the certainties of other people, and to rest always in the darker side of possibility. But if anything may be true, surely the beautiful may be true, the good, the joyous, the lovable, as well as the gloomy and despondent.

And if the privilege of scepticism is hope, the essence of it is questioning and questing. There is a doubt which, in its despair of ultimate truth, is content to trifle, to beguile the misery of life with jest and play and momentary diversion. Or there is the doubt in deeper matters which, as with Darwin, turns to eager, assiduous investigation of the mere, fascinating detail of the external world. But there is also a doubt which lives in passionate, perpetual earnestness and the unfailing, unyielding, indomitable effort to find out God, being assured that without Him the universe, with all its splendor and all its endless evolving glory, is nothing, merely nothing. Such doubt will express itself in words like those of the modern poet:

'Day and night I wander widely through the wilderness of
    thought,
Catching dainty things of fancy most reluctant to be caught.
Shining tangles leading nowhere I persistently unravel,
Tread strange paths of meditation very intricate to travel.

Gleaming bits of quaint desire tempt my steps beyond the
    decent.
I confound old solid glory with publicity too recent.
But my one unchanged obsession, whereso'er my feet have
    trod,
Is a keen, enormous, haunting, never-sated thirst for God.'

THE END

BOOKS BY DARWIN, WITH THE ABBREVIATIONS USED IN REFERRING TO THEM IN THE NOTES

The American revised edition is referred to, unless otherwise specified

*A Monograph on the sub-class Cirripedia.
— The Balanidæ — The Verrucidæ.* — *Cirripedia.*

The Descent of Man and Selection in Relation to Sex. — *Descent.*

The Different Forms of Flowers on Plants of the Same Species. — *Different Forms of Flowers.*

The Effects of Cross and Self Fertilization in the Vegetable Kingdom. — *Cross and Self Fertilization.*

Krause, Ernst, *Erasmus Darwin* (translated from the German by W. S. Dallas, with a preliminary notice by Charles Darwin). — *Krause.*

The Expression of the Emotions in Man and Animals. — *Expression.*

The Formation of Vegetable Mould through the Action of Worms. — *Worms.*

Geological Observations. — *Geological Observations.*

Insectivorous Plants. — *Insectivorous Plants.*

Journal of Researches into the Natural History and Geology of the Countries Visited during the Voyage of H.M.S. Beagle Round the World. — *Beagle Journal.*

More Letters of Charles Darwin, two volumes. — *More Letters.*

The Movements and Habits of Climbing Plants. — *Climbing Plants.*

The Origin of Species. — *Origin.*

The Power of Movement in Plants. — *Movement in Plants.*

The Variation of Animals and Plants under Domestication, two volumes. — *Animals and Plants.*

The Various Contrivances by which Orchids are Fertilized by Insects. — *Orchids.*

BOOKS BIOGRAPHICAL AND CRITICAL MOST FREQUENTLY REFERRED TO IN THE NOTES, WITH THE ABBREVIATIONS USED

Aristotle, *Historia Animalium*, translated by D'Arcy Wentworth Thompson. *Historia Animalium.*

Castle, W. E., *Genetics and Eugenics.* *Genetics and Eugenics.*

Conklin, Edwin Grant, *The Direction of Human Evolution.* *Evolution.*

Darwin, Emma, *A Century of Family Letters*, two volumes. *Family Letters.*

Darwin, *The Life and Letters of Charles Darwin*, two volumes. *Life.*

De Vries, Hugo, *Species and Varieties, Their Origin by Mutation.* *Species and Varieties.*

Goncourts, Edmond et Jules, *Journal des Goncourts*, nine volumes. *Goncourts, Journal.*

Gray, Asa, *Letters of*, edited by Jane Loring Gray, two volumes. *Gray Letters.*

Grant Duff, Sir Mountstuart E., *Notes from a Diary*, fourteen volumes, 1851-1901. *Grant Duff.*

Huxley, Thomas H., *Darwiniana* (the second volume of Collected Essays). *Darwiniana.*

Huxley, Thomas H., *Life and Letters of*, by his son Leonard, two volumes. *Huxley, Life.*

Lull Richard, Harry Burr Ferris, George Howard Parker, James Rowland Angell, Albert Galloway Keller, Edwin Grant Conklin, *The Evolution of Man.* *Lull.*

Morgan, Thomas Hunt, *Evolution and Adaptation.* *Evolution and Adaptation.*

Osborn, Henry Fairfield, *The Earth Speaks to Bryan.* *The Earth Speaks.*

Osborn, *From the Greeks to Darwin.* *Greeks to Darwin.*

BOOKS BIOGRAPHICAL AND CRITICAL

Osborn, Henry Fairfield, *Impressions of Great Naturalists.* *Great Naturalists.*

Parker, George Howard, *What Evolution Is.* *What Evolution Is.*

Pearson, Karl, *The Grammar of Science.* *Grammar of Science.*

Thoreau, Henry, *Journal*, fourteen volumes. *Journal.*

Vallery-Radot, Pasteur. *Vallery-Radot, Pasteur.*

Wallace, Alfred Russell, *My Life*, two volumes. Wallace, *Life.*

Whitehead, Alfred North, *Science and the Modern World.* *Science and the Modern World.*

NOTES

CHAPTER I: THE OBSERVER

1. *Journal des Goncourts*, May 1, 1857, vol. I, p. 182.
2. Ben Jonson, *The Poetaster*, act II, scene I.
3. *Sentimental Journey*, 'In the Street.'
4. *Portraits Littéraires*, vol. III, p. 546.
5. *Expression*, p. 80.
6. Thoreau, *Journal*, vol. VII, p. 46.
7. Gray, to Darwin, May 18, 1862, Gray, *Letters*, vol. II, p. 481.
8. *Great Naturalists*, p. 51.
9. *More Letters*, vol. I, p. 72.
10. *Life*, vol. I, p. 83.
11. To Farrar, November 26, 1868, *Life*, vol. II, p. 453.
12. To Hooker, 1867, *More Letters*, vol. II, p. 6.
13. To Lyell, June 1, 1867, *Life*, vol. II, p. 248.
14. To Wilson, April 29, 1878, *More Letters*, vol. II, p. 421.
15. To Galton, November, 1879, *Life*, vol. II, p. 414.
16. To Lyell, March 17, 1863, *Life*, vol. II, p. 201.
17. To Galton, November 8, 1872, *More Letters*, vol. II, p. 108.
18. *Expression*, p. 184.
19. To Dr. Ogle, March 12, 1871, *Life*, vol. II, p. 321.
20. *More Letters*, vol. I, p. 4.
21. To Jenyns, October 17, 1846, *Life*, vol. I, p. 396.
22. *Beagle Journal*, p. 282.
23. To Gray, June 3, 1874, *Life*, vol. II, p. 457.
24. To Hooker, December 11, 1860, *Life*, vol. II, p. 148.
25. To Scott, July 2, 1863, *More Letters*, vol. II, p. 323.
26. To Horner, January, 1847, *More Letters*, vol. II, p. 224.
27. *Expression*, p. 12.
28. *Life*, vol. II, p. 238.
29. *More Letters*, vol. II, p. 105.
30. *Life*, vol. I, p. 40.
31. *Different Forms of Flowers*, p. 189.
32. To Wiesner, October 4, 1881, *More Letters*, vol. II, p. 432.

33. *Life*, vol. I, p. 124.
34. *Ibid.*
35. *Life*, vol. I, p. 125.
36. *Life*, vol. II, p. 453.
37. *Cirripedia*, p. 155.
38. To Lyell, September 12, 1860, *Life*, vol. II, p. 133.
39. *Darwiniana*, p. 275.
40. To Hooker, February 4, 1861, *Life*, vol. II, p. 153.
41. To Lyell, March 9, 1850, *More Letters*, vol. II, p. 229.
42. *Life*, vol. I, p. 125.
43. *Life*, vol. I, p. 105.
44. *Life*, vol. I, p. 80.
45. *Life*, vol. I, p. 121.
46. *Purgatorio*, canto III.
47. To Miss S. Darwin, August 4, 1836, *Life*, vol. I, p. 237.
48. To Hooker, 1847, *Life*, vol. I, p. 317.
49. *More Letters*, vol. I, p. 3.
50. To Miss C. Darwin, November 8, 1834, *Life*, vol. I, p. 230.
51. *Beagle Journal*, p. 78.
52. *Life*, vol. I, p. 109.
53. *Expression*, p. 194.
54. To Romanes, May 29, 1876, *More Letters*, vol. I, p. 364.
55. To Fox, May, 1832, *Life*, vol. I, p. 206.
56. To Henslow, May 18, 1832, *Life*, vol. I, p. 208.
57. To Henslow, August 15, 1832, *More Letters*, vol. I, p. 9.
58. *Journal*, August 29, 1858, vol. XI, p. 137.
59. *Journal*, December 4, 1856, vol. IX, p. 158.
60. *Life*, vol. I, p. 368.
61. *Worms*, p. 97.
62. *Origin*, p. 105.
63. In *Popular Science Monthly*, April, 1909, vol. LXXIV, p. 198.

CHAPTER II: THE THINKER

1. To Bates, November 22, 1860, *More Letters*, vol. I, p. 176.
2. To Fawcett, September 18, 1861, *More Letters*, vol. I, p. 195.
3. *More Letters*, vol. I, p. 93.

NOTES

4. *Life*, vol. I, p. 40.
5. Answer to questionnaire, *Life*, vol. II, p. 355.
6. *Life of Huxley*, vol. I, p. 521.
7. To Wallace, August 28, 1872, *Life*, vol. II, p. 346.
8. To Balfour, September 4, 1880, *More Letters*, vol. II, p. 424.
9. *Beagle Journal*, p. 378.
10. To Wallace, December 22, 1857, *Life*, vol. I, p. 465.
11. *Journal*, March 23, 1853, vol. V, p. 45.
12. Gray to Canby, July 14, 1874, Gray, *Letters*, vol. II, p. 649.
13. Gray to Darwin, July 21, 1863, Gray, *Letters*, vol. II, p. 509.
14. *Life*, vol. I, p. 79.
15. To Fox, March 24, 1859, *Life*, vol. I, p. 506.
16. *Life*, vol. I, p. 83.
17. To Hooker, February, 1846, *More Letters*, vol. I, p. 56.
18. To Wallace, February 26, 1867, *Life*, vol. II, p. 276.
19. *Grammar of Science*, p. 38.
20. To Huxley, December 2, 1860, *Life*, vol. II, p. 147.
21. To Hooker, November 15, 1855, *More Letters*, vol. I, p. 84.
22. To Gray, November 29, 1859, *More Letters*, vol. I, p. 126.
23. *Beagle Journal*, p. 443.
24. *Life*, vol. I, p. 83.
25. Thiselton Dyer, in *Life*, vol. II, p. 431.
26. To Gray, 1857, *More Letters*, vol. II, p. 252.
27. To Hooker, January 11, 1844, *More Letters*, vol. I, p. 39.
28. To Wallace, May 1, 1857, *Life*, vol. I, p. 454.
29. To Carpenter, November 19, 1859, *Life*, vol. II, p. 19.
30. To Huxley, May 27, 1865, *Life*, vol. II, p. 228.
31. Aristotle, *Historia Animalium*, Book I, chapter VI.
32. *Life*, vol. I, p. 126.
33. To Hooker, April 14, 1855, *Life*, vol. I, p. 415.
34. To Hooker, March 26, 1863, *More Letters*, vol. I, p. 474.
35. *Genetics and Eugenics*, p. 181.
36. De Vries, *Species and Varieties*, p. 769.
37. *Different Forms of Flowers*, p. 156.
38. To Gray, April 3, 1860, *Life*, vol. II, p. 90.
39. *Zur Naturwissenschaft, Einzelne Betrachtungen und Aphorismen*, section III.

NOTES

40. *Life*, vol. I, p. 121.
41. To Wiesner, October 25, 1881, *Life*, vol. II, p. 510.
42. *Life*, vol. I, p. 122.
43. *Orchids*, p. 208.
44. To Huxley, November 27, 1859, *Life*, vol. II, p. 75.
45. *Insectivorous Plants*, p. 154.
46. To Gray, June 8, 1860, *More Letters*, vol. I, p. 153.
47. Huxley to Romanes, May 9, 1882, *Life of Huxley*, vol. II, p. 42.
48. Huxley to Foster, February 14, 1888, *Life of Huxley*, vol. II, p. 203.
49. Huxley to Hooker, March 9, 1888, *Life of Huxley*, vol. II, p. 204.
50. *Darwiniana*, p. 287.
51. Alexander Agassiz to Gibbs, December 15, 1897, in G. R. Agassiz, *Letters and Recollections of Alexander Agassiz*, p. 333.
52. J. J. Stevenson, in *Popular Science Monthly*, April, 1909, vol. LXXIV, p. 353.
53. October 2, 1879, *Life*, vol. II, p. 360.
54. May 5, 1881, *More Letters*, vol. II, p. 198.
55. *Descent*, p. 606.
56. September 23, 1868, *More Letters*, vol. II, p. 85.
57. August 19, 1868, *More Letters*, vol. II, p. 84.
58. To Wallace, April 30, 1868, *More Letters*, vol. II, p. 77.
59. To Huxley, June 12, 1867, *More Letters*, vol. I, p. 281.
60. *Animals and Plants*, vol. II, p. 396.
61. *Animals and Plants*, vol. II, p. 399.
62. *Life*, vol. I, p. 75.
63. August Weisman, *The Evolution Theory* (translation Thomson), vol. I, p. 242.
64. *Darwiniana*, p. 20.
65. To Hooker, January 20, 1859, *Life*, vol. I, p. 499.
66. *Life*, vol. I, p. 77.
67. Vallery-Radot, *Pasteur*, p. 139.
68. *Life*, vol. I, p. 71.
69. To Lyell, September 20, 1859, *Life*, vol. I, p. 521.
70. *Life*, vol. I, p. 130.
71. *Life*, vol. I, p. 117.
72. July 2, 1860, *Life*, vol. II, p. 116.

73. To Lyell, August 1, 1845, *Life*, vol. I, p. 308.
74. To Hooker, September 25, 1853, *Life*, vol. I, p. 400.
75. *Origin*, p. 404.
76. To Hooker, October, 1856, *Life*, vol. I, p. 443.
77. To Henslow, *Life*, vol. I, p. 245.
78. To Huxley, July 3, 1860, *Life*, vol. II, p. 117.
79. *Life*, vol. I, p. 72.
80. To Lyell, October 1, 1861, *More Letters*, vol. II, p. 191.
81. *Zur Naturwissenschaft, Einzelne Betrachtungen und Aphorismen*, section III.
82. To Hooker, December 10, 1866, *Life*, vol. II, p. 239.
83. To Hooker, May 2, 1857, *Life*, vol. I, p. 454.
84. *Darwiniana*, p. 246.
85. To De Candolle, January 14, 1863, *More Letters*, vol. I, p. 234.
86. To Hooker, April 1, 1864, *More Letters*, vol. II, p. 330.
87. To Hooker, April, 1857, *Life*, vol. I, p. 450.
88. To Hooker, March 7, 1855, *Life*, vol. I, p. 405.
89. To Hooker, July 30, 1856, *Life*, vol. I, p. 439.
90. To Huxley, January 10, 1863, *More Letters*, vol. I, p. 231.

CHAPTER III: THE DISCOVERER

1. *Historia Animalium*, book VIII, chapter XXVIII.
2. *Historia Animalium*, book VIII, chapter XXIX.
3. *Beagle Journal*, p. 216.
4. To Hooker, January 11, 1844, *Life*, vol. I, p. 384.
5. To Hooker, November, 1844, *More Letters*, vol. I, p. 43.
6. To Lyell, October, 11, 1859, *Life*, vol. II, p. 10.
7. *Greeks to Darwin*, p. 156.
8. *Greeks to Darwin*, p. 233.
9. To Lyell, March 12, 1863, *Life*, vol. II, p. 199.
10. Marcus Herzog, introduction to Samuel Butler's *Unconscious Memory*, p. XII.
11. To Lyell, March 17, 1863, *Life*, vol. II, p. 201.
12. *More Letters*, vol. I, p. 37.
13. *MS. Journals*, in *Life*, vol. I, p. 363.
14. To Horace Darwin, December 15, 1871, *Family Letters*, vol. II, p. 207.

NOTES

3. *Life*, vol. I, p. 81.
4. *Life*, vol. I, p. 81.
5. *Life*, vol. I, p. 30.
6. To Lyell, January 22, 1865, *Life*, vol. II, p. 216.
7. To Morley, March 24, 1871, *More Letters*, vol. I, p. 326.
8. Lull, p. 129.
9. To Hooker, December 21, 1859, *Life*, vol. II, p. 21.
10. To Hooker, September 27, 1865, *Life*, vol. II, p. 225.
11. To Henslow, May 18, 1832, *Life*, vol. I, p. 220.
12. *Life*, vol. II, p. 356.
13. To Herbert, June 2, 1833, *Life*, vol. I, p. 210.
14. *Reminiscences of Charles Darwin*, in *Harper's Magazine*, December, 1909, vol. cxx, p. 15.
15. To Müller, August 28, 1870, *More Letters*, vol. II, p. 92.
16. *Beagle Journal*, p. 499.
17. *Life*, vol. II, p. 377.
18. *Descent of Man*, p. 70.
19. *Life*, vol. II, p. 309.
20. To Wallace, July 12, 1881, in Wallace, *Life*, vol. II, p. 15.
21. To Wallace, July 12, 1881, in Wallace, *Life*, vol. II, p. 14.
22. To Lyell, January 22, 1865, *Life*, vol. II, p. 217.
23. *Krause*, p. 70.
24. Emma Wedgwood to Madame Sismondi, November 15, 1838, *Family Letters*, vol. II, p. 7.
25. To Gurney, July 8, 1876, *Life*, vol. II, p. 364.
26. *Family Letters*, vol. II, p. 171.
27. *Life*, vol. I, p. 103.
28. *Ibid.*
29. *Beagle Journal*, p. 112.
30. *Life*, vol. I, p. 43.
31. *Life*, vol. I, p. 42.
32. To Susan Darwin, April 23, 1835, *Life*, vol. I, p. 233.
33. *Life*, vol. I, p. 146.
34. *Life*, vol. I, p. 42.
35. *Life*, vol. I, p. 81.
36. *Life*, vol. II, p. 178.
37. To Mrs. Haliburton, November 22, 1880, *Life*, vol. II, p. 508.

NOTES

38. To Henslow, July 24, 1834, *More Letters*, vol. I, p. 14.
39. To Hooker, March 17, 1867, *More Letters*, vol. II, p. 2.
40. To Rivers, December 28, 1866, *Life*, vol. II, p. 241.
41. *Darwiniana*, p. 286.
42. *Life*, vol. I, p. 102.
43. *Life*, vol. I, p. 81.
44. *Ibid.*
45. *Life*, vol. I, p. 57.
46. *Life*, vol. I, p. 81.
47. E. B. Titchener, in *Popular Science Monthly*, January, 1909, vol. LXXIV, p. 47.
48. *Causeries du Lundi*, vol. IV, p. 45.
49. To Newton, May 3, 1780, *The Correspondence of William Cowper* (edition Wright), vol. I, p. 185.
50. *Poems* (Globe edition), p. 191.
51. *Childe Harold*, canto III, stanza 72.
52. Sénancour, *Obermann*, p. 40.
53. *Life*, vol. I, p. 95.
54. To Mrs. Darwin, April, 1858, *Life*, vol. I, p. 471.
55. *Beagle Journal*, p. 322.
56. To Henslow, August 15, 1832, *More Letters*, vol. I, p. 10.
57. *Family Letters*, vol. II, p. 175.
58. Mrs. Darwin to Darwin, 1859, *Family Letters*, vol. II, p. 175.
59. *Family Letters*, vol. II, p. 201.
60. *Beagle Journal*, p. 263.
61. *Life*, vol. II, p. 308.
62. *Ibid.*
63. *Descent of Man*, p. 612.
64. *Life*, vol. II, p. 238.
65. *Life*, vol. II, p. 237.
66. William Darwin, in *Family Letters*, vol. II, p. 169.
67. *Expression*, p. 219.
68. *Beagle Journal*, p. 411.
69. *Life*, vol. I, p. 29.
70. *Life*, vol. I, p. 282.
71. To Lyell, September 3, 1874, *More Letters*, vol. II, p. 237.
72. *Family Letters*, vol. II, p. 253.

NOTES

73. To Ridley, November 28, 1878, *Life*, vol. II, p. 412.
74. To Gray, July, 1860, *Life*, vol. I, p. 284.

CHAPTER V: THE LOVER

1. Norton to Ruskin, September 9, 1868, *Letters of Charles Eliot Norton*, vol. I, p. 309.
2. *Great Naturalists*, p. 57.
3. *Reminiscences of Charles Darwin*, in *Harper's Magazine*, December, 1909, vol. CXX, p. 13.
4. To Francis Darwin, November 11, 1887, *The Life and Letters of Leslie Stephen*, by Frederic William Maitland, p. 393.
5. To Norton, *Life of Stephen* as above, p. 300.
6. To Falconer, November 8, 1864, *More Letters*, vol. I, p. 257.
7. Norton, Diary, April 12, 1873, in *Letters of Charles Eliot Norton*, vol. I, p. 477.
8. Kingsley to Lubbock, in *Life of Sir John Lubbock, Lord Avebury*, by Horace G. Hutchinson, vol. I, p. 92.
9. Grant Duff, *Diary, 1873-1881*, December 15, 1880, vol. II, p. 283.
10. July, 1860, *More Letters*, vol. I, p. 159.
11. September 5, 1862, *More Letters*, vol. I, p. 205.
12. To Hooker, April 23, 1861, *More Letters*, vol. I, p. 185.
13. To Fox, March 13, 1837, *Life*, vol. I, p. 249.
14. *Life*, vol. I, p. 42.
15. *Life*, vol. I, p. 28.
16. *Life*, vol. I, p. 49.
17. *Life*, vol. I, p. 89.
18. *Life*, vol. I, p. 30.
19. *Life*, vol. I, p. 96.
20. Answer to questionnaire, *Life*, vol. II, p. 415.
21. To Mrs. Darwin, March, 1842, *Family Letters*, vol. II, p. 69.
22. To Fox, March 24, 1859, *Life*, vol. I, p. 506.
23. January 28, 1876, *Family Letters*, vol. II, p. 221.
24. To Hooker, September 1, 1859, *Life*, vol. I, p. 518.
25. *Life*, vol. I, p. 85.
26. To Falconer, November 14, 1862, *More Letters*, vol. I, p. 211.

NOTES

27. To Hooker, May 29, 1854, *More Letters*, vol. I, p. 79.
28. *Life*, vol. I, p. 243.
29. *Life*, vol. I, p. 197.
30. To Hooker, November, 1863, *Life*, vol. II, p. 186.
31. To Henslow, May 6, 1849, *More Letters*, vol. I, p. 66.
32. *Life*, vol. I, p. 96.
33. *Diary, 1892-1895*, August 6, 1892, vol. I, p. 80.
34. Emma Wedgwood to Madame Sismondi, November 15, 1838, *Family Letters*, vol. II, p. 7.
35. To Hooker, April 10, 1846, *More Letters*, vol. I, p. 416.
36. To Murray, 1859, *Life*, vol. I, p. 532.
37. *Life*, vol. I, p. 99.
38. *Life*, vol. I, p. 98.
39. *Life*, vol. I, p. 99.
40. *Reminiscences*, in *Harper's Magazine*, December, 1909, vol. cxx, p. 17.
41. Grant Duff, *Diary, 1896-1901*, vol. I, p. 307.
42. *Life*, vol. I, p. 118.
43. *Life*, vol. I, p. 115.
44. *Life*, vol. I, p. 28.
45. November, 1855, *More Letters*, vol. I, p. 87.
46. To Hooker, September 27, 1865, *Life*, vol. II, p. 223.
47. *Family Letters*, vol. II, p. 118.
48. January 20, 1839, *More Letters*, vol. I, p. 29.
49. *Ibid.*
50. *Family Letters*, vol. II, p. 48.
51. September 5, 1862, *More Letters*, vol. I, p. 204.
52. *More Letters*, vol. I, p. 30.
53. *Ibid.*
54. *Life*, vol. I. p. 135.
55. To Madame Sismondi, February, 1840, *Family Letters*, vol. II, p. 51.
56. *Life*, vol. I, p. 109.
57. *Family Letters*, vol. II, p. 253.
58. To Gray, July 23, 1862, *More Letters*, vol. I, p. 202.
59. *Diary of Thomas Moore*, August 29, 1822, vol. III, p. 367.
60. *Life*, vol. I, p. 112.

NOTES

61. *Life*, p. III.
62. *Life*, vol. I, p. 115.
63. *Life*, vol. I, p. 10.
64. *Life*, vol. I, p. 76.
65. *Family Letters*, vol. II, p. 44.
66. December 18, 1861, *More Letters*, vol. II, p. 281.
67. To Wallace, February 27, 1868, *More Letters*, vol. I, p. 289.
68. *Life*, vol. I, p. 115.
69. Krause, p. 29.
70. *Life*, vol. I, p. 31.
71. *Life*, vol. I, p. 119.
72. *Life of Sir John Lubbock, Lord Avebury*, by Horace G. Hutchinson, vol. I, p. 40.
73. To Hooker, July 28, 1859, *More Letters*, vol. I, p. 126.
74. To Hooker, April 14, 1855, *Life*, vol. I, p. 415.
75. To Hooker, November 5, 1853, *Life*, vol. I, p. 356.
76. September 11, 1859, *Life*, vol. I, p. 520.
77. To Hooker, May 25, 1870, *Life*, vol. II, p. 306.
78. To Müller, June 21, 1881, *More Letters*, vol. II, p. 369.
79. Huxley to Mivart, November 12, 1885, *Life of Huxley*, vol. II, p. 122.
80. To Hooker, July 2, 1860, *Life*, vol. II, p. 116.

CHAPTER VI: THE DESTROYER

1. To Hooker, December 5, 1863, *More Letters*, vol. II, p. 337.
2. *Life*, vol. I, p. 279.
3. *Descent*, p. 145.
4. In *Life*, vol. II, p. 245.
5. To Hooker, July 13, 1856, *More Letters*, vol. I, p. 94.
6. In *Nature*, 1882, vol. XXVI, p. 5, quoted in *Encyclopædia Brittanica* (edition 1884), *Supplement*, article *Darwinism*.
7. *Origin*, p. 429.
8. To Gray, September 17, 1861, *Life*, vol. II, p. 170.
9. To Hooker, March 29, 1863, *Life*, vol. II, p. 202.
10. *Descent of Man*, p. 121.
11. *Descent of Man*, p. 612.

NOTES

12. *Origin*, p. 164.
13. *Descent of Man*, p. 100.
14. *Life*, vol. II, p. 347.
15. To Hooker, February 9, 1865, *More Letters*, vol. I, p. 260.
16. To Lyell, August 21, 1861, *More Letters*, vol. I, p. 194.
17. To Gray, May 22, 1860, *Life*, vol. II, p. 105.
18. *Descent of Man*, p. 612.
19. *Animals and Plants*, vol. II, p. 428.
20. *Family Letters*, vol. II, p. 196.
21. To Scherzer, December 26, 1879, *Life*, vol. II, p. 413.
22. August Weisman, *The Evolution Theory* (Translation Thomson), vol. II, p. 364.
23. Address on Darwin Centenary, in *Contemporary Review*, July, 1909, vol. XCVI, p. 21.
24. Herbert Spencer, *An Autobiography*, vol. II, p. 548.
25. *The Earth Speaks*, p. 63.
26. In *Boston Herald*, June 3, 1926.
27. Lull, p. 146.
28. *Saturday Review of Literature*, editorial, May 29, 1926.
29. Reverend Charles G. Finney, *Memoirs, Written by Himself*, p. 171.
30. Jules Lemaître, *Impressions de Théatre*, vol. IV, p. 114.
31. *Life*, vol. II, p. 239.
32. Answers to Questions, in *Boston Herald*, January 4, 1926.
33. To Hooker, January 19, 1865, *More Letters*, vol. I, p. 260.
34. *Evolution*, p. 247.
35. Conklin, *Evolution*, p. 240.
36. *La Grande Duchesse de Gérolstein*, act IV, scene 3.
37. *Palinodia*.
38. *La Ginestra*.
39. Ernest Renan, *Drames Philosophiques*, p. 174.
40. Ernest Renan, *Drames Philosophiques*, p. 178.
41. *Anatole France Himself*, by J. J. Brousson (translation Pollock), p. 71.
42. *The Mysterious Stranger*, p. 150.
43. *Sopra un Basso Relievo Antico Sepolcrale*.

NOTES

CHAPTER VII: THE SCIENTIFIC SPIRIT

1. To Scott, June 6, 1863, *More Letters*, vol. II, p. 323.
2. To Huxley, *More Letters*, vol. I, p. 125.
3. Hooker on Darwin, *Life*, vol. I, p. 315.
4. To Huxley, July 20, 1860, *More Letters*, vol. I, p. 158.
5. To Günther, May 15, 1870, *Life*, vol. II, p. 303.
6. To Dohrn, January 4, 1870, *More Letters*, vol. II, p. 444.
7. *Science and the Modern World*, p. 255.
8. Article by J. E. Harry, on the *Helena* of Euripides, in *Journal of American Philology*, October, 1925, vol. XLVI, p. 332.
9. Speech at Royal Society Anniversary Dinner, 1894, Huxley, *Life*, vol. II, p. 413.
10. To Hooker, July 28, 1868, *More Letters*, vol. I, p. 305.
11. To Farrar, August 28, 1881, *More Letters*, vol. I, p. 394.
12. To Hooker, March 3, 1860, *Life*, vol. II, p. 85.
13. To Lubbock, November 12, 1859, *Life*, vol. II, p. 14.
14. To Carpenter, November 19, 1859, *Life*, vol. II, p. 19.
15. To Madame d'Epinay, July 6, 1766, *Correspondance de Voltaire* (edition 1881), vol. XII, p. 329.
16. To Hooker, 1856, *More Letters*, vol. I, p. 90.
17. To Wiesner, October 25, 1881, *Life*, vol. II, p. 508.
18. To Bentham, November 25, 1869, *More Letters*, vol. I, p. 379.
19. To Wilson, March 5, 1879, *More Letters*, vol. II, p. 422.
20. Darwin to Wallace, August 8, 1872, *Life*, vol. II, p. 348.
21. Vallery-Radot, *Pasteur*, p. 22.
22. To Henslow, April 1, 1848, *More Letters*, vol. I, p. 61.
23. *Portraits Littéraires*, vol. III, p. 546.
24. *Port-Royal*, vol. I, p. 55.
25. *Causeries du Lundi*, vol. II, p. 268.
26. *Portraits Contemporains* (1882), vol. V, p. 461.
27. *Portraits Littéraires*, vol. III, p. 543.
28. *Portraits Contemporains* (1882), vol. V, p. 465.
29. *Portraits Contemporains* (1882), vol. V, p. 464.
30. *Portraits Littéraires*, vol. III, p. 543.
31. *Journal des Goncourts*, vol. II, p. 134.

NOTES

32. *Conversations with Eckermann*, quoted in William James, *Varieties of Religious Experience*, p. 137.

33. *Port-Royal*, vol. VI, p. 245.

34. To Helvetius, January 5, 1740, *Correspondance* (edition 1881), vol. III, p. 356.

35. Quoted by Sainte-Beuve, *Causeries du Lundi*, vol. VII, p. 47.

36. *Tristram Shandy*, Book VII, chapter XXXIII.

37. *Maximen und Reflexionen*, chapter III.

38. *Journal de Henri Frédéric Amiel*, vol. I, p. 129.

39. *Discoveries*, in Jonson's Works (edition Cunningham), vol. III, p. 401.

40. *Homeric Epigrams* (edition Baumeister), v.

INDEX

Abstemiousness, D.'s, 182.

Accuracy, D. and, in observation, 21; in statement, 22, 23; mathematical, and instruments, 24; his hobby, 59.

Achievement, motives, 96–99; D.'s attitude, 99–101.

Adams, Henry, effect of evolution on, 242.

Æsthetics, observation in, 11; D.'s attitude, 137; effect of scientific spirit, 272, 275.

Agassiz, Alexander, on D.'s coral-reef theory, 65; on D. and candor, 105.

Agassiz, Louis, and evolution, 103.

Agnosticism, as dogma, 283, 284.

Agriculture, revolution, 11.

Ambition, as trait, D. on it, 96.

Amiel, H. F., self-dissection, 280.

Animals, D.'s love, 135, 188.

Appearance, D.'s, 168.

Appreciation, D.'s trait, 79, 80; element in scientific spirit, 263.

Architecture, D.'s attitude, 139.

Ardor, element in scientific spirit, 264.

Argument, D.'s attitude, 74.

Aristotle, on experiment, 56; and evolution, 84.

Arnold, Matthew, on Goethe, 271.

Art, D.'s attitude, 138–40; evolution and realism, 225.

Barnacles, D.'s study, 26.

Bates, H. W., and nature, 12.

Beagle, D.'s voyage, 4.

Bell, Thomas, and D., 173.

Bergson, Henri, and evolution, 235.

Bryce, Lord, on D. and Gladstone, 133; on D.'s appearance, 168.

Buckle, H. T., D. on, 143.

Buffon, Comte de, and evolution, 84, 119.

Burbank, Luther, and experiment, 57; and future life, 228.

Butler, Samuel, D.'s controversy, 108; and religion and evolution. 237.

Byron, Lord, and nature, 152.

Candor, D.'s trait, 77–79, 105.

Castle, W. E., on experiment, 57.

Caution, element in scientific spirit, 245. *See also* Deduction.

Chambers, Robert, and evolution, 84.

Children. *See* Family.

Civil War, D.'s interest, 134.

Collecting, D. and, 43.

Comparison, D.'s trait, 31.

Conklin, E. G., on natural selection, 125; on evolution and religion, 239.

Conscience, activity of D.'s, 160.

Controversy, over evolution, 6; D.'s attitude, 76, 77, 107.

Conversation, D.'s, 170.

Coolidge, Calvin, on politics and religion, 222.

Copernicus, and orthodoxy, 209.

INDEX

Coral reefs, D.'s theory, 64–66.

Correspondence, character of D.'s, 78, 145.

Cowper, William, and nature, 149, 150.

Creation, desire, 98.

Criticism, D.'s attitude, 104–17.

Cruelty, D.'s hatred, 135.

Curiosity, element of scientific spirit, 248, 249; Sainte-Beuve and Goethe and, 268, 270.

Darwin, Charles R., influence, 3; character, 3; birth, 3; ancestry, 3; education, 4, 45; interest in outdoor life and sport, 4, 174–76; *Beagle* voyage, 4, 14; marriage, home and children, family life, 4, 196–201; invalidism, patience, 5, 36, 177–83, 193–95; tomb, 6; scientific observation, on it, 6, 14–16; and self-analysis, 16; study of expression, 17–19, 198; promotion of observation by others, 19, 23; accuracy, 21–24, 59; and detail, 25; industry and patience, 27–30, 252; system, 30, 31, 183; element of comparison, 31; difficulties and discomforts of outdoor observation, 32–34; sympathy, and observation, 34–36; effect of physical limitations, 36, 37; and collecting, 43; and observation and deduction, 44–46, 250; on Spencer, 47, 78; and deduction and induction, 46–48; mental power and activity, 48; control over theorizing, 51, 54, 55, 115, 124; on excessive theorizing, 52, 53, 254; and experiment, 56–62; exposition, style, cau-

tion, 62–64, 143–45, 212; on coral reefs, 64–66; on sexual selection, 66, 67; on pangenesis, 68; and metaphysics, 69; doubt and self-criticism, 70, 71; and objections and difficulties, 71, 72, 113–15; and revision, 73, 118; and argument, 74–76; and controversy, 76, 107; and mistakes, 77; candor, 77–79, 105; as correspondent, 78, 145; appreciation and tolerance, 79, 80, 262, 263; and ignorance and deceptive reasoning, 80–82; and motives of achievement, 99–101; Butler controversy, 108; humility, 110, 258, 260; success of books, 122; fame, 126; atrophy of other interests, 128–30, 272, 275; and history, 130, 131; and politics, 131–34; and Civil War, 134; and slavery, 134; and animals, hatred of cruelty, 135, 188; and vivisection, 136; and social questions, 136, 137; and æsthetics, 137–40; and music, 140–42; and fiction, 145; and poetry, 146–48; and natural beauty, 148, 153–56; and religion and conscience, 156–63; personal appearance, 168; hospitality, 169; conversation, 170–72; fun, 172; and society, 173, 178; humanity, 176; abstemiousness and indulgence, 182; regimen, 183; finances, 184–86; generosity, 186; manner and temperament, 188; and his father, 190; as fiancé, 190–92; as husband, wife's care, 192–94; friendship and services, 201–07; impartiality, 256; on scientific ardor, 264; on

308

love of truth, 266. *See also* Evolution.

Darwin, Emma (Wedgwood), 4; and theater, 139; and D.'s religious attitude, 157; D. as fiancé, 190–92, and as husband, 192; as wife, and D.'s invalidism, 193–96; and D.'s theories, 218.

Darwin, Erasmus, 4; and evolution, 84, 85; controversy over biography, 108.

Deduction, observation and, 44–46; and induction, 46–48; D.'s attitude, 46, 47; D.'s power, 48–50, 69; his control over it, 51, 54, 55, 115, 124; D. on excessive, 52, 53; types of thinkers, 53–55; experiment and, 55; D. and experiment, 56–62; D. and exposition, 62–64; illustrations of his theorizing, 64–69; D. and doubt, 70, 71; D. and objections, 71, 72; his trait of revision, 73; D. and arguments, 74–77; D. and mistakes, 77; D. and deception in reason, 80–82, 115. *See also* Observation; Scientific spirit.

Democracy, evolution and, 223.

Details, D. and, 25.

De Vries, Hugo, imitation theory, 124.

Discipline, D. and his children, 197.

Doubt, value, 70; in D.'s logical processes, 70, 71; aspects of agnosticism, 203–05. *See also* Religion.

Drink, D. and, 182.

Earthworms, D.'s study, 21, 42, 151.

Education, D.'s, 4; training in deduction, 45.

Eliot, C. W., effect of evolution on, 246.

Emerson, R. W., on evolution, 42, 234; and nature, 151.

Empedocles, and evolution, 84.

Ethics, D. and morality, 160; and evolution, 213–15, 219, 222, 231.

Evolution, idea and D.'s explanation of process, 4; controversy, 6; acceptance of principle, 6, 121, 125; effect on study of natural history, 40–43; as term, 83; before Darwin, 83–85, 101, 233; theory of inheritance of acquired characters, D. and, 85, 87; D. and predecessors, 85–88; beginning of D.'s interest, 88; his development of theory of natural selection, 89–91; his statement of theory, 91; his realization of influence of theory, 92, 209–13; his years of study and experiment, 92, 93; Wallace and presentation of theory, 93, 94; D. and Wallace, 94, 95; *Origin of Species*, its effect, 96; D.'s attitude toward, as achievement, 99–101, 122–24; attacks by scientists, 102; religious attacks, 103; D. and attacks, 104–08; D. and other workers, 109; D. and difficulties, 111–17; D.'s revisions, 118; modification of theory, 119–21, 124; promulgators, 121; effect on theology, 209; D.'s caution in statement, 212; D. and ethical standards under theory, 213; D. and effect on belief, 215, 216; **D.** and belief in God, 216–18; and atheism, 218–20; as typifying scientific influence on life, 221; influence on politics, 222–25; and realism, 225; and hell and heaven, 227; and popular belief in God and worship, 229, 230; and substitute for sin, 231–33; philosophical, 233–35; clerical harmonizing with religion, 236; Fundamentalists and, 237, 282; scientific harmonizing, 237–39; and individualism in religious belief, 239, 240; future adjustment with religion, 240; destructive spiritual effect, 241–47; self-contradictions in reason, 280.

Experiment, D.'s devotion, 5, 56; position, 55; equipment, 57; **D.**'s thoroughness, 58; impersonality, 58; accuracy, repetition, 59; recording, errors and successes, 61.

Exposition, D.'s power, 62–64; illustrations, 64–69.

Expression, D.'s study, 17–19.

Eye, and evolutionary theory, 112.

Fabre, J. H., and nature, 12.

Fame, as motive of achievement, 96–101.

Family, D. and father's memory, 190; D. as fiancé, 190–92; husband and wife, 192–96; children, training, 196–201; their assistance, 200.

Farrer, Sir Thomas, on D.'s detailed observation, 26.

Fichte, J. H. von, and evolution, 233.

Fiction, D.'s attitude, 145.

Financial condition, D.'s, 184; his attitude and care, 185; his generosity, 186.

Finney, C. G., on revival, 230.

Fiske, John, and evolution, 122, 241.

France, Anatole, effect of evolution on, 242.

Friendship, D.'s trait, 201, 202; his influence over friends, 202; his dependence, 203; his services to friends, 204–07.

Fun, D.'s trait, 172.

Fundamentalism, attacks on evolution, 103, 282; ethical attitude, 232; theological attitude, 237.

Gautier, Théophile, on observation, 7; as poet, 11.

Generosity, D.'s trait, 186.

George, Henry D. and *Progress and Poverty*, 137.

Gladstone, W. E., and D., 133.

God, D.'s attitude, 164–67; influence of evolution on belief, 216–18, 229; thirst for, 285.

Goethe, J. W. von, on repetitions, 59; on doubt, 70; on mistakes, 77; and evolution, 85; and poetry, 148; on love of truth, 265; and scientific spirit, 270, 271; pessimism, 274; on active ignorance, 279.

Gould, George M., on D.'s invalidism, 180.

Grant Duff, Sir M. E., on D., 182.

Gray, Asa, on D.'s observation, 14; on D. as thinker, 49; relations with D., 110; and evolution, 121, 238.

INDEX

Häckel, Ernst, and D., 110; and evolution, 122; atheism, 219.

Hartmann, K. R. E. von, and evolution, 233.

Hegel, G. W. F., type, 53; and evolution, 233.

Hell, obsolete, 227.

History, D. and, 130, 131.

Homer, on self-ignorance, 282.

Hooker, Sir Joseph, on Darwin-Wallace paper, 94; and D., 101, 110.

Hospitality, D.'s, 169.

Humanity, and study of natural history, 40–43, 136; Sainte-Beuve's study, 267, 268.

Humility, D.'s trait, 110; and scientific spirit, 257–61.

Huxley, T. H., on D. and detailed observation, 26; on D.'s industry, 27; and induction, 46; on D.'s mental processes, 62; on D.'s candor, 79; on effect of *Origin of Species*, 96; and Bishop of Oxford's attack, 103; restraint of D., 108; on D. and adverse suggestions, 115; and promulgation of D.'s theory, 121; on D.'s style, 144; relations with D., 203–05; on influence of D.'s appreciation, 206; and religion, 219; on D.'s impartiality, 256.

Ibsen, Henrik, effect of evolution on, 241.

Ignorance, realization and scientific spirit, 257, 283.

Imagination. *See* Deduction.

Immortality, D.'s attitude, 163; effect of evolution, 215.

Impartiality, element in scientific

spirit, 255; Sainte-Beuve and, 268.

Induction, and deduction, 46–48. *See also* Deduction.

Industry, D.'s, 27; element in scientific spirit, 251.

Inheritance of acquired characters, Lamarck's theory, 85, 90; D.'s attitude toward, 87, 119, 120.

Instruments, D.'s faith, 25.

Instinct in practical life, 278, 279.

Interests, absorption and atrophy, 128–30, 272.

Invalidism, D.'s, 5, 36, 177; his attitude toward it, 178, 179, 194; cause, 179–81; Mrs. D.'s care, 193–96.

James, William, and evolution, 234.

Jeffries, Richard, and nature, 12.

Jonson, Ben, on observation, 7; on self-ignorance, 282.

Kingsley, Charles, on evolutionary theory, 121; on D.'s conversation, 171.

Knowledge, and observation, 38–40; and wisdom, 44.

Krause, Ernst, biography of Erasmus Darwin, 108.

Lamarck, Jean de, evolutionary theory, 85, 90, 119, 120; D.'s attitude, 86.

Land question, D. and, 136.

Leibnitz, Baron von, and gravity, 257.

Leopardi, Giacomo, pessimism, 238, 245.

Literature, D.'s attitude, 143,

145–48; D.'s style, 143–45; effect of evolution, 225–27.

Linnæan Society, Darwin-Wallace paper, 94.

Lodge, Sir Oliver, and science and spiritualism, 238.

Love, D.'s valuation, 206. *See also* Family; Friendship.

Lubbock, Sir John, on debt to D., 202.

Lucretius, type, 54; scientific ardor, 265.

Lyell, Sir Charles, on controversy, 76; and evolution, 84; and D., 101, 110; on D. and 'remorse,' 211.

McDougall, William, on inheritance of acquired characters, 85.

Maine de Biran, self-dissection, 280.

Manner, D.'s, 188.

Marriage of cousins, D. and, 136.

Mendel, Gregor, experiments, 124.

Milton, John, D.'s appreciation, 146.

Missing links in evolutionary theory, 113.

Missionaries, D.'s attitude, 159.

Mistakes, D.'s attitude, 77.

Mivart, St. G. J., and evolution and religion, 238.

Montesquieu, on study, 277.

Moody, D. L., absorption of interest, 129; and prayer, 162; and God, 167; and hell and heaven, 227, 228.

Moore, Thomas, on children, 196.

Morality. *See* Ethics.

Morgan, Lloyd, and evolution, 235.

Music, D.'s attitude, 140–42.

Native, utilitarian and æsthetic observation, 10–13; D. and appreciation, 148, 153–56; elements of enjoyment, 149–53.

Natural selection, D.'s term and theory, 5, 90; modification of theory, 119–21, 124. *See also* Evolution.

Neuter insects, and evolutionary theory, 113.

Nietzsche, F. W., effect of evolution on, 241.

Norton, C. E., on D., 168, 170.

Objections, in D.'s logical processes, 71.

Observation, D.'s scientific trait, 6, 14, 19–21; as general trait, 6–8; by women, 8; exclusive, 8; of humanity, 9, 267, 268; of nature, change in character, 10; ulterior, 11; æsthetic, 11; delight, 12, 38, 148–54; Thoreau, 13; D.'s comments, 15; D.'s general trait, 16; his study of expression, 17–19; D. and accuracy, 21; accuracy in statement, 22–24; D. and information from others, 19, 23; mathematical, and instruments, 24; detailed, 25; D.'s industry and patience, 27–29; need of patience, 29; system, 30, 31; comparison, 31; difficulties and discomforts, 32–34; and sympathy, 34–36; effect of D.'s physical limitations, 36, 37; knowledge as aid, 38–40; effect of evolution on, 40-43. *See also* Deduction; Scientific spirit.

Origin of Species, publication,

INDEX

effect, 5, 96; exposition, 63; revisions, 73, 118; success, 122.

Osborn, H. F., on D.'s observation, 14; on D. and Lamarck, 87; on D. and criticism, 105; on D.'s change in attitude, 120; on D.'s fame, 124; on D.'s appearance, 168; on ethical effect of evolution, 222.

Owen, Sir Richard, and evolution, 103, 107, 111.

Oxford, Bishop of, attack on evolution, 103.

Pangenesis, D.'s theory, 68.

Parker, G. H., on evolution, 125.

Pascal, Blaise, on man, 275.

Pasteur, Louis, and objections, 72; scientific ardor, 265.

Patience, D.'s, 28; element in scientific spirit, 29, 253.

Pearson, Karl, on D. and imagination, 51.

Pedantry, and scientific spirit, 257.

Perry, R. B., on evolution, 125.

Pessimism, and evolution, 233; Sainte-Beuve's, 272, 276; Goethe's, 274.

Philosophy, D. and self-analysis, 16; D. and metaphysics, 69; evolutionary, 233.

Poetry, D.'s attitude, 146–48; Sainte-Beuve and, 268.

Politics, D. and, 131–33; influence of evolution, 222.

Pragmatism, and evolution, 234.

Prayer, D.'s attitude, 161–63.

Primogeniture, D.'s attitude, 136.

Pugnacity, and scientific spirit, 261.

Realism, as fruit of evolution, 225.

Reason, and instinct, 277–79; as agent of scientific spirit, 279; evolutionary contradictions, 280, 282; and attainment of truth, 281. *See also* Deduction; Scientific spirit.

Religion, D.'s attitude, 156–67; pre-Darwinian theology, 208; and Copernicus's speculations, 209; theological effect of evolution, 209; D.'s attitude toward effect, 209–13; ethical standards under evolution, 213–15, 219; evolution and belief in future life, 215, 216; and belief in God, 216–18, 229; and democracy, 223; evolution and hell and heaven, 227, 228; fundamentalism, 232, 237, 282; clerical harmonizing with evolution, 236; scientific harmonizing, 237–39; egocentric *versus* ethnocentric, 239, 240; persistence, 240; thirst for God, 285.

Renan, J. E., effect of evolution on, 241.

Research, element in scientific spirit, 250.

Revision, D.'s trait, 73, 118; element in scientific spirit, 255–57.

Royer-Collard, Paul, on facts, 44.

Ruskin, John, on vision of artists, 11.

St.-Hilaire, Auguste, and evolution, 85.

Sainte-Beuve, C. A., observation of humanity, 9, 267, 268; type, 54; on absorption of interest, 128; and poetry, 148, 268; and scientific spirit, 266–70; concreteness, 269; on Goethe, 271; pessimism and sexual immorality, 272–74, 76.

Schelling, F. W. J. von, and evolution, 233.

Scherer, Edmond, on tolerance, 262; on man, 275.

Schopenhauer, Arthur, and evolution, 233.

Scientific spirit, motives of achievements, 96–101; 248, 249; research, 250; industry, 251–53; patience, 253; caution, 254; flexibility and impartiality, 255; lack of pedantry, 257–59; and human nature, 259, 262; humility, 260; tolerance, 261; and pugnacity, 261; appreciation, 263; ardor, 264; illustrations: Sainte-Beuve, 266–70; Goethe, 270, 271; and spiritual blight, 272–76; inadequacy, 277; and instinctive action, 278, 279; reason as agent, 279; and self-dissection, 279; and selfcontradictions, 280; and unattainable truth, 281–83; and ignorance and hope, 283–85. *See also* Deduction; Observation.

Scott, Sir Walter, industry, 252.

Sedgwick, Adam, and D., 205.

Self-dissection, as betrayal of scientific spirit, 279.

Sénancour, É. P. de, on nature, 153; self-dissection, 280.

Sexual selection, D.'s theory, 66, 67.

Shakespeare, William, vitality, 126; D.'s opinion, 147.

Shaw, G. B., and religion and evolution, 237.

Shelley, P. B., and nature, 152.

Sin, effect of evolution on belief, 231.

Slavery, D.'s antipathy, 134.

Smoking, D. and, 182.

Snuff, D.'s indulgence, 183.

Socialism, and evolution, 224.

Society, D. and, 173, 178.

Spencer, Herbert, and 'survival of the fittest,' 5, 91; D. on, 47, 78; type, 54; and universal evolution, 121, 219.

Spinoza, Baruch, type, 53.

Spiritualism, and evolution, 238.

Sport, D.'s attitude, 174–76.

Statement, accuracy, 22–24.

Stephen, Leslie, on D., 169.

Sterne, Laurence, on observation, 7; on doing, 277.

Study. *See* Observation.

Survival of the fittest. Spencer's term, 5, 91.

Sympathy, and observation, 34–38.

System, D. and, 30, 183.

Theater, D.'s attitude, 139.

Theology. *See* Religion.

Thoreau, H. D., and observation of nature, 13; on knowledge as aid to observation, 39; and deduction, 48.

Thrift, self-contradiction, 280.

Tolerance, D.'s trait, 79, 80; element in scientific spirit, 261–63.

Tolstoi, Leo, effect of evolution on, 241.

Torrey, Bradford, on observation, 8.

Truth, instinct as element in scientific spirit, 265, 275; Goethe's characteristic, 270;

INDEX

unattainable, 281–83; ignorance and hope, 283–85.

Turner, Sir William, on D. and
information, 24.

Twain, Mark, effect of evolution
on, 243.

Vivisection, D.'s attitude, 136.

Voltaire, and tolerance, 261; on
study, 277.

Wallace, A. R., on collecting, 43;
and D.'s sexual-selection theory, 66, 67; and presentation of
evolutionary theory, 93, 94;
relations with D., 94, 95; and
spiritualism, 238.

Water cure, D.'s subjection to,
181.

Wedgwood, Emma, Mrs. Dar-
win, 4.

Weisman, August, on deduction,
70; and evolution, 122, 218.

Wells, H. G., and religion and
evolution, 237.

Westminster Abbey, D.'s tomb, 6.

White, Gilbert, and nature, 12.

Whitehead, A. N., on D.'s caution, 125; and evolution, 235,
246; on scientific flexibility,
255.

Wiesner, Julius, courtesy, 262.

Wisdom, and knowledge, 44. *See
also* Deduction.

Wordsworth, William, and nature, 151.

Zola, Émile, as realist, 226, 241.

DATE DUE